The Sheffield College

AN INTRODUCTION TO

sports mechanics

A home study pack providing sportspeople with
an introduction to the basic mechanics of movement

ISBN 1-902523-64-4

Author: Karen Sprunt
Based on material written by David Kerwin, Mike Lindsay and John Newton

Revised for 3rd edition by Neil Fowler

Editors: Penny Crisfield, Nicola Cooke
Typesetter: Jo Willard
Illustrations: William Rudling
Cover photo courtesy of actionplus sports images

sports coach UK
114 Cardigan Road
Headingley
Leeds LS6 3BJ
Tel: 0113-274 4802 Fax: 0113-275 5019
E-mail: coaching@sportscoachuk.org
Website: www.sportscoachuk.org

Patron: HRH The Princess Royal

In conjunction with

sportscotland
Caledonia House
South Gyle
Edinburgh EH12 9DQ

Published on behalf of
sports coach UK by

Coachwise Solutions
Coachwise Ltd
Chelsea Close
Off Amberley Road
Armley
Leeds LS12 4HP
Tel: 0113-231 1310 Fax: 0113-231 9606
E-mail: enquiries@coachwisesolutions.co.uk
Website: www.coachwisesolutions.co.uk

Preface

This home study pack, produced by the National Coaching Foundation in conjunction with **sport**scotland, complements two other packs in the series: *An Introduction to the Structure of the Body* and *An Introduction to Sports Physiology.*

It is intended for anyone (coach, teacher, performer), who wishes to understand the principles which explain how the body and other objects move in sporting situations. Understanding these principles can guide the development of correct and efficient technique and reduce the risk of injury. Each chapter provides information, activities and questions to help you. If this information is new to you, the pack will probably take about 12–15 hours to complete.

By completing the pack, you will be able to generate some evidence towards the underpinning knowledge and application required for the Level 3 National Occupational Standards for Coaching, Teaching and Instructing (see Appendix D for further details).

To help you, a set of multiple choice questions and a case study are provided in Appendix C.

Key to symbols used in the text

 An activity.

 Approximate length of time to be spent on the activity.

 Stop and consider.

 Self tester questions to check your own understanding.

Throughout this pack, the pronouns he, she, him, her and so on are interchangeable and intended to be inclusive of both men and women. It is important in sport, as elsewhere, that men and women have equal status and opportunities.

Contents

Introduction

1.0 What's in It for You?

This home study pack is produced in conjunction with **sport**scotland. Each chapter provides information, activities and exercises to illustrate key issues, and a self-tester to measure your understanding. From time to time, you will be directed to other material to broaden your knowledge or follow a particular issue in more depth.

This chapter will explain the purpose of the study pack and provide an overview of the mechanical principles that will be developed in later chapters. By the end of the pack, you should:

- have worked through a number of basic mechanical principles which are relevant to sports performance
- have guidelines which will help you analyse your sport more objectively
- be able to use the results of your analysis to decide whether any changes should be made to a technique to make it more effective.

Why is this Pack Important for Sportspeople?

A knowledge of the principles that govern how the body moves can lead to the development of safe and efficient technique, which may increase the likelihood of success and reduce the risk of injury. This pack is only intended to provide an introduction to mechanical principles relevant to sports performance. Often you will be asked to think about how the information relates to your own sport and sometimes you will be directed to senior coaches in your sport for further information. If you want to study the mechanical principles in more depth, or learn about a wider range of topics, the references at the end of each chapter will direct you to the appropriate sources of information.

What Knowledge is Needed to Work Through this Pack?

Not a lot – the course is written assuming no prior knowledge of sports mechanics. However, it is assumed you have already studied the NCF Introductory Study Pack *Improving Techniques* or have attended the NCF Introductory Workshop *Improving Techniques,* and that you are involved in sport perhaps as a participant, leader, teacher or coach. The questions at the end of this chapter are designed to help you check your own knowledge and give reassurance that you will be able to complete the pack successfully.

1.1 Getting Started

Biomechanics sounds like a very complex subject and one that is full of long, technical words, complex theories and unrelated facts. Do not be put off. This pack is designed to introduce you to the principles that will help you gain a better understanding of the techniques and movements of your sport. Jargon is avoided where possible and movement principles are explained through the use of everyday and sports examples. Nevertheless, some technical terms will need to be used from time to time but usually these explanations are provided in panels. All terms are explained in a glossary at the back, so you can refer to them as often as you need. There is a space left there for you to add any other terms that are new to you as you meet them in the text. If you prefer, you can set up your own glossary (see Activity 1) and build this using your own words and examples. You may find that you want to modify your explanations as you develop a better understanding while working through the pack.

ACTIVITY 1

Use an A4 sheet of paper (the same size as this book) and keep it with you as you work through the pack. Print each term as you meet it in the text and write in a definition using your own words.

For example:

Biomechanics   The study of the principles which explain how the human body moves or stays at rest.

Forces   Get things moving, stop things moving (eg push, pull), change the rate at which or direction in which objects move.

Learning about the field of sports mechanics is a little like tackling a jigsaw – you have to start somewhere, gradually building up the picture. Inevitably it does not make complete sense until every piece is in place. You will have to be patient and willing to accept some pieces of information, knowing that it will make better sense when you have all the pieces once you have worked through the whole pack.

It is useful to start by thinking about the basic techniques and movements that are required in your sport. It may be helpful to picture a performer in action – what sort of techniques do they use? What sort of movements are necessary? What parts of the body are used? Many sports involve running but think how it may vary, for example, in your sport:

- do the performers need to run at a constant speed?
- do they stop and start, speed up and slow down?
- do they move in a straight line?
- is striking, lifting or throwing involved?

Try Activity 2.

ACTIVITY 2

1   Make a list of all the basic movements which form part of your sport in the left-hand column below. Try to be specific. For example, do not just write **run** if you mean **running at different speeds** which involves speeding up and slowing down; instead of **stand**, think about whether the person needs to be **balanced** or **ready to move**.

Movements in Your Sport	Movements in Different Sports

2   When you have finished your own sport, think about a contrasting sport of which you have some knowledge. For example, if your sport is a team game or racket sport, you might choose a highly technical sport such as athletics, swimming or gymnastics (and vice versa). Try to work out the movements required in this sport and write them down in the right-hand column.

3   Highlight or circle movements that seem to be common to both.

Now turn over.

Your list will probably have included movements such as:

- *sprinting*
- *speeding up*
- *slowing down*
- *stopping*
- *starting*
- *changing direction*

- *striking*
- *pushing*
- *pulling*
- *sliding*
- *lifting*
- *resisting movement*

- *turning*
- *twisting*
- *jumping*
- *throwing*
- *maintaining balance.*

Underline any movements listed above that were not relevant to either of your sports.

Add to Activity 1 any of these movements you omitted but are required in the sport you analysed.

Add to the list above any movements you wrote down which you feel should be included.

Perhaps you are surprised about the range of movements needed by your sport or about the number of movements common to different sports. Sports movements may look somewhat different partly because they take place in their own setting, with their own unique set of rules and with their own special equipment. However, if you start to analyse the movements required, you will see that some types of movement occur again and again in different situations and rely on the same underpinning principles of movement. Can you think of these principles?

Some types of movement occur again and again.

ACTIVITY 3

Look at the list of things on the previous page that the human body is able to do.

What makes these things happen? What makes things move or stop?

Now turn over.

You will probably have suggested that force causes the body to move or stay still, or causes some other object (eg a ball) to move.

1.2 Forces

You were introduced to the concept of force in the NCF Introductory Study Pack *Improving Techniques*. What can forces do?

Forces are needed to make the body start to move:

- How does a sprinter move forward off the blocks?
  By pushing back against the blocks.

- How does a basketball player jump up for a rebound?
  By pushing down against the floor.

- How does a swimmer move forward through the water?
  By pushing back against the water.

Forces are needed to make the body stop or slow down:

- How does a netball player stop travelling when catching the ball?
  By pushing against the ground.

- How does a gymnast stop after a vault?
  By pushing hard against the mat.

- How does a skier stop at the end of the race?
  If there is no incline, the skier must turn the skis sideways and push against the snow.

Forces are needed to keep the body still:

- How does a pistol shooter hold his/her arm so still?
  The shoulder and arm muscles produce a force that balances the downward pull of gravity.

- How does a tug of war team resist being dragged forward?
  They pull on the rope, balancing the force produced by the opposition.

- How does a judo player resist being thrown?
  By anticipating the opponent's move and pulling or pushing in the opposite direction.

Forces are needed to make the body change direction:

- How does a high jumper produce the required lift at the end of the approach run?
  By pushing down against the ground to jump upwards.
- How does a rugby player swerve to avoid a tackle?
  By pushing sharply off one foot to move in the opposite direction.
- How does a skater create a spin on the ice?
  By pushing back against the ice with the toe of one skate at the same time as moving forward to initiate a spin on the other skate.

Forces are needed to move an external object:

- How does a golfer drive the ball from the tee onto the fairway?
  By using the muscles to swing the club and exert a force on the ball.
- How is an arrow made to move?
  The force from the stretched bowstring propels the arrow forward.
- How does a windsurfer skim across the water?
  The wind catches in the sail and pushes it along.

What happens in your sport? Try the next activity.

ACTIVITY 4

Beside each of the following statements, write down a specific example from your sport. Remember, they may not all be relevant.

Forces are Needed to:	Example in Your Sport
make the body start to move	
make the body stop or slow down	
keep the body still	
make the body change direction	
move an external object	

The **study of sports mechanics** is really the study of the effect of forces acting on the body. These include:

- internal forces (like those produced by the muscles)
- external forces (eg gravity, air resistance).

In Chapter Two, forces will be studied in more detail. You will consider different types of forces that affect movement and discover how to apply force efficiently in your sport.

Once you have worked through this chapter, you may wish to return to Activity 4 to check your answers. The rest of the pack looks at the various effects produced by applying forces in different ways, different directions and different places:

- Stability
- Momentum and impulse
- Angular motion
- Projectiles.

Each of these will be introduced in separate chapters, as you gradually build up the whole jigsaw of the mechanics which underpin movement in sport.

1.3 Stability

A stable object is one which is difficult to disturb or knock off balance. Understanding stability is important in sport because it enables the performer to resist motion, to be motionless or ready to move into action.

ACTIVITY 5

Write down an example from your sport where you need to:

• move the body quickly:

• hold the body motionless:

• resist a force exerted on you by an opponent:

You will have an opportunity to check your answers in Chapter Three, when the factors that affect stability will be considered. These include the:

• position of the object's centre of gravity
• size of the object's base of support.

You will be able to identify techniques in your sport in which these factors are important, become more skilled at analysing these factors and then at working out how to modify technique appropriately.

1.4 Momentum and Impulse

Momentum is all about the movement that is produced as a result of forces being applied. In Chapter Four, you will look at how to apply forces both to the body and to other objects to produce specific effects. For example, how to apply forces to:

• gain the greatest height or distance (eg high jump, javelin, volleyball block)
• move heavy objects (eg weightlifting, judo, scrummaging in rugby)
• stop objects safely and effectively (eg catching in cricket, stopping the ball in hockey, landing in gymnastics).

ACTIVITY 6

What happens in your sport? Do you need to gain height or distance, move a heavy object or stop an object? Write down examples of each in the table below (leave the right-hand column blank for now):

Objective	Example from Your Sport	S/R
Gain height		
Gain distance		
Move heavy object		
Stop an object		

Look back at your list of examples and note how many involve movement in a straight line and how many involve rotation. Place an S (straight line) or R (for rotation) in the right-hand column beside each example.

You may wish to return to check your examples once you have worked through Chapter Four.

1.5 Angular Motion

You will probably have felt that most of your examples in Activity 6 involved moving in straight lines or curved lines. However, if you study movement carefully, you will find that many sports actually involve some form of rotation. For example:

- running often occurs in a straight line but the movement is created by rotation of the limbs

- in a tennis drive, the arm swings through an arc rotating around the shoulder

- rotation is created in many sports by imparting spin to the ball (eg football, cricket).

In Chapter Five, you will study how rotation is created, why some things are more difficult to rotate than others, and how to modify technique to gain the right amount of rotation. By the end of Chapter Five, you should be able to describe how rotation is imparted or prevented, and identify techniques in your sport where rotation is important.

In many sports the performer needs to be able to make an object (eg ball, discus) spin. So having learned how to create rotation, you also need to understand what happens to rotating objects once they are in the air. This is referred to as the study of projectiles.

1.6 Projectiles

Chapter Six concentrates on the movement of balls in the air. This chapter will be most relevant to those involved in ball games. You will look at:

• how an object is projected into the air

• how the object is slowed down in the air (drag forces)

• why some objects travel through the air more easily than others (eg table tennis balls and golf balls)

• how balls swerve in flight (lift forces).

1.7 The Final Jigsaw

Once you have worked through these chapters, you will have many of the jigsaw pieces in place. Chapter Seven shows you how to apply all these principles to your own sport, analyse techniques more objectively and identify possible ways to modify technique to improve performance.

Before moving on to further chapters, it is important to check your current level of knowledge by completing Self Tester 1.

SELF TESTER FOR CHAPTER ONE

1 In many of the activities within this pack you will be asked to analyse techniques from your own sport, so it is important that you have an effective, systematic approach to observation and analysis. The following seven sentences provide a strategy for analysing performance that you were introduced to in the NCF Introductory Study Pack *Improving Techniques*. However, the sentences are not in the correct order. Check that you can remember the steps in analysis by numbering each sentence to show the correct order. For example, if you think the first stage is allowing the performers to practise, place a 1 in the box beside this sentence.

- Give the performer feedback explaining what has to be done to correct the problem. ☐

- Identify the root of the problem. ☐

- Break the technique down into simple parts. ☐

- Re-evaluate the performer's technique. ☐

- Identify the technique to be analysed. ☐

- Allow the performer to practise. ☐

- Rate the effectiveness of the performer at each part of the technique. ☐

2 You should also be familiar with the terms **force, stability** and **centre of gravity**. Write a brief explanation of each term in the spaces provided below.

   • Force:

   • Stability:

   • Centre of gravity:

Now turn over.

1 *Put the following sentences in the correct order to produce a strategy for analysing performance:*

- *Identify the technique to be analysed.*
- *Break the technique down into simple parts.*
- *Rate the effectiveness of the performer at each part of the technique.*
- *Identify the root of the problem.*
- *Give the performer feedback explaining what has to be done to correct the problem.*
- *Allow the performer to practise.*
- *Re-evaluate the performer's technique.*

2 *Write a brief explanation of each of the following terms:*

- *Force:*

  This can be explained as a push or a pull. It is what gets things moving or stops things moving.

- *Stability:*

  This is a measure of how well an object resists being bowled over, or made to move in a different direction, or at a different speed.

- *Centre of gravity:*

  This is an imaginary point at which all the mass of a body or object can be considered to act.

If you had any difficulty with this self tester, go back and reread the relevant parts before moving on to the next chapter.

Getting Things Moving (Forces)

2.0 Introduction

As mentioned in Chapter One, forces make things happen and stop things happening, make things move and stop things moving. Good technique depends in part on being able to apply forces at the right place and in the right direction, so it is important to understand the way forces are applied.

In this chapter, you will look more carefully at the forces operating in sport. By the end of this chapter, you should be able to:

- give a working definition of force
- list the forces that affect performance
- describe the effects that forces may have on objects
- differentiate between internal and external forces
- explain how internal forces are used to generate external forces
- use the knowledge you gain to analyse where force is applied, in what direction, and how much force is applied in your sport.

In many ways, this chapter serves as a building block to help you use the later chapters and apply all the principles of mechanics to your sport. It provides some of the first pieces of the jigsaw but remember you may not see the full picture until you have worked right through the pack.

2.1 Defining Force

Force is a word used in everyday language. Forces were mentioned in Chapter One but what does the word really mean to you? Try Activity 7.

ACTIVITY 7

1 Without looking it up in a dictionary, write down what you think the word **force** means:

2 Now check what the dictionary says. There is probably a range of definitions but write down the one that seems to match your understanding of the word in the way that it has been used so far in this pack:

Now turn over.

Now study the two definitions of force below from biomechanists.

A body's state of being at rest or in motion can be changed by the action of some other body. The pushing or pulling effect that this other body has, and that causes the change, is termed a force.

James Hay, 1993

Force is that which causes or tends to cause a change in a body's motion or shape.

Kreighbaum and Barthels, 1985

You will find a number of different definitions – check yours against them. Does it mean the same things? Choose one of the two definitions above that you find easy to understand and write it down in your own glossary.

How is force measured? You will be familiar with measuring time in seconds using a stopwatch and distance in metres using a tape measure, but you may not know that you can measure forces in newtons using a force plate (see Panel A).

Panel A: Units of Force and Force Plates

Force is measured in newtons (N) (after Sir Isacc Newton). A newton is defined as the force required to give a mass of one kilogram an acceleration of one metre per second per second.

If you stand on a set of bathroom scales, the reading you see is a measure of the downwards force caused by your body weight. For a person with a mass of 80kg, the downwards force would be approximately 800 newtons.

Bathroom scales can only measure forces in the vertical direction. They cannot provide information about the horizontal forces acting forwards and backwards on the body, or those acting from left to right. In sport, we are interested in these forces and so need some means of measuring them.

To do this, sport scientists use a device called a force platform. You may have seen one in a laboratory or on the television. They are a little like bathroom scales, but are able to measure forces in three dimensions (see Figure 1):

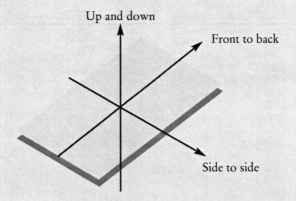

Figure 1: Force can be measured in three dimensions using a force platform

Force platforms can therefore be used to measure not only the size of the force, but also the direction in which it is applied.

When a person walks, runs over or jumps on to the platform, the forces applied to the platform are measured in three directions and recorded by microcomputer. A computer is required because these forces are constantly changing. If you stand on your bathroom scales and rapidly bend your knees, you will see the dial move as the force changes. To see these changes in force, the output from force platforms is most commonly viewed as a force-time graph.

You will sometimes need to measure force accurately (eg to determine the pressure[1] of a ball, the tension in racket strings, the pressures involved in scuba diving). More frequently, you will need to be able to identify the relevant forces operating in your sport and know how to create the movement you want by applying the:

- right amount of force
- force at the right place
- force in the right direction.

The next activity will help you to think about the types of forces influencing sports performance.

Applying the right amount of force in the right place in the right direction helps techniques.

---

1   Pressure is the ratio of force to the area over which the force is applied.

ACTIVITY 8

Jot down the major force operating:

- on a springboard diver after leaving the board:

- between the sole of your shoe and the sports hall floor to prevent your shoe from slipping:

- against you when you are running into a headwind:

- inside your body enabling you to swing a racket, throw or kick a ball, or jump a hurdle:

Now turn over.

The major forces you should have identified are:

- *gravity (the force that pulls the diver and all other objects down towards the centre of the earth)*
- *friction (the force that prevents your shoe from slipping)*
- *air resistance (the opposing force presented by the air, through which the athlete must run)*
- *muscular force (the force produced by muscle contraction).*

The following section looks briefly at gravity, friction, muscular forces and air resistance, and considers how these affect sports performance. Air resistance will be dealt with more fully in Chapter Six.

2.2 The Force of Gravity

You may be surprised to know that every object in the universe exerts an attractive force on every other object in the universe. The size of this attractive force depends on the mass[1] of the two objects and the distance between them.

Usually this force is very small. Look around at the objects in the room. They are all exerting an attractive force on you and you are exerting an attractive force on them. The reason you do not feel anything and nothing moves is because the masses involved are far too small and the distances are far too great (in relation to the masses) to cause any noticeable effect.

However, the Earth has a vast mass and you are very close to it. The attractive force it exerts on you and all the objects around you is very noticeable. Gravity keeps objects on the Earth's surface, and gravity brings things down to ground level when they are dropped or thrown in the air.

If you need a more precise definition of the force of gravity, read Panel B.

Panel B: Gravity

Newton's Law of Gravitation explains that any two particles of matter attract one another with a force directly proportional to the product of their masses and inversely proportional to the square of the distances between them.

---

1   Mass refers to the composition of the object or the quantity of matter of which an object is composed. Write this in your glossary of terms.

There are several things to remember about gravity:

- Gravity acts on you all the time – whether you are sitting still, jumping upwards from a trampoline or flying in a hang-glider.

- Gravity always pulls objects and people downwards towards the centre of the Earth. More accurately, gravity accelerates (or tends to accelerate) all objects towards the centre of the Earth at a rate of approximately 9.81 metres per second per second.

- The effect of gravity becomes smaller as you move further from the centre of the Earth. Would this significantly affect sports performances at altitude? (See Panel C for an answer.)

- Gravity exerts a downward pull on every particle of matter in your body. The greater your mass, the greater the total pulling effect of gravity. This pulling effect is called your weight. The Moon has a smaller mass than the Earth and would exert a much weaker downward pull on each particle of matter in your body – the gravitational pull of the Moon is about 1/6 of the Earth. This means that you would weigh less on the Moon than on the earth but your mass would have stayed the same.

Panel C: The Reduced Effect of Gravity at Altitude

The effect of gravity decreases as you move further away from the centre of the Earth (eg at the top of a mountain or at a high city like Mexico City). The Earth has a radius of about 10,000km. Travelling to Mexico City would only take you an extra 2.2km away from the centre of the Earth, reducing the effect of gravity by 0.05%. If a footballer was to kick a ball 70m this would make a difference of less than 25cm.[1]

You need to understand gravity because it influences all sports activities. When you try to move any object upwards (eg when you jump, throw or lift), you are trying to exert forces to overcome gravity. Chapter Four explains how to do this effectively and Chapter Six explains how you can predict the flight path of airborne objects. When you try to move things downwards (eg downhill skiing, bowling in cricket, serving in tennis), you are working with gravity. In all these situations, it is vital to exert forces at the correct place and in the right direction to gain the best effect. This will be considered again later in this chapter. Try the next activity to see if you can identify situations in your sport when you are overcoming or working with gravity.

---

1   Further examples are given in Daish, CB (1972) **The physics of ball games.** London, English Universities Press. ISBN 0-3400-53992.

ACTIVITY 9

Write down a situation in your sport when it is important to be able to:

• overcome gravity

• use gravity

You will have realised that gravity is important in your sport and probably had little or no difficulty in identifying situations[1]. Now you can move on to examine friction, the next piece of the jigsaw.

2.3 Friction Force

Friction is the force created between two contacting surfaces that tend to rub or slide past each other – your shoe on the ground or the floor, your hands on the racket or stick, your skate on the ice.

If you put this pack on a table and pull it towards you, the frictional force would be acting in the opposite direction – away from you. Friction tends to resist such sliding or slipping – the strength of the resistance depends on the surfaces. This is very important, for in many situations you will want to avoid slipping. For example:

• in changing direction on a squash court or swerving in rugby or hockey

• the first few strides in a sprint start or any burst of acceleration

• maintaining a grip in pole-vaulting, racket sports and rowing.

1   If you had any difficulty, it may help to go back and reread Section 2.2.

In some situations, you need to be able to slip and slide. For example:

- in winter sports such as skating, skiing or bob-sleigh
- sliding into a tackle in soccer or into a tennis shot on a shale court
- between the moving parts of a bicycle, gun or boat.

 Stop to think of an example of each from your own sport.

The amount of friction created between two surfaces depends on several factors:

- **Surface texture.** Even the smoothest surface has bumps and grooves that catch the bumps and grooves on the other surface. The rougher or stickier the surface, the more the bumps and grooves catch and prevent slipping and the greater the friction between the two surfaces.

- **Pressing two surfaces together increases the friction** between the two surfaces. The greater the force pressing the surfaces together, the more the bumps and grooves of the surfaces interlock. For example, if you grip the racket handle tightly, it is less likely to slip when you strike the ball.

If you want to know more about the friction between two surfaces, read Panel D.

Panel D: Friction

Surface texture and surface hardness determine a quantity called the **coefficient of friction**, which indicates how easily objects can slide over that surface. A slippery surface (such as ice) has a low coefficient of friction; a surface that gives a good grip (like a running track) has a high coefficient of friction.

The force pressing two surfaces together is called the **normal force** or the **perpendicular force**.

The relationship between the coefficient of friction (μ), the normal force (R) and the frictional force (F) produced is expressed by the equation:

$$F = \mu R$$

You might assume that friction is decreased by reducing the area of the two surfaces in contact. This is not the case. For example, a racing car with wide tyres does not experience greater frictional forces than if fitted with narrower tyres travelling on the same surface. When it has the narrow tyres fitted, the greater pressure flattens the surface in contact with the road, causing more bumps and grooves to come into contact with the road surface. This increase in actual contact area compensates for the loss in apparent contact area and frictional forces remain the same. Similarly, athletes could not increase the friction created simply by wearing bigger shoes.

A racing car with wide tyres does not experience greater frictional force.
Similarly, an athlete cannot increase the friction created by wearing bigger shoes.

There is also a difference in the friction developed as you try to slide an object and the friction that exists once the object is sliding. Try the next activity and this will become clear to you.

ACTIVITY 10

Is there more than one sort of friction? Place a heavy book on the table and push it with your index finger. Try this several times and then describe what happens. Pay particular attention to how hard you push and how easily the book moves.

1 What happened?

2 Why?

Now turn over.

*You will have found that the book did not immediately move when you pushed it. Did you notice a gradual increase in how hard you pushed until the book suddenly slid forwards? If not, go back and try again – a heavier book may make things more obvious. When you pushed the book and it stayed still, **static** friction was preventing it from moving. Once you started the book moving, you should have found that less push was required to keep it moving. The friction that operates when an object is moving is called **dynamic** or **sliding** friction. This second type of friction is less resistant than static friction.*

Forces are exerted in many ways.

ACTIVITY II

Consider the following situation and then answer the questions. Picture a games player pushing off quickly, seeming to start off well but then suddenly losing his/her footing and falling forward.

1 Describe what is happening while the push is effective:

2 Describe what happens to cause the player to fall forwards:

Now turn over.

1   *Static friction prevents the foot from slipping.*

2   *The player overcomes static friction. Dynamic friction offers much less resistance to the thrust. Because the player is still pushing hard, the foot suddenly slips completely away from him/her.*

There was not enough friction between the shoe and the ground for the player's push to remain effective. You need to be able to make friction work in your favour (ie to increase or decrease it) to match the demands of the situation.

Reducing and Increasing Friction

How can you alter friction forces? Work through Activity 12.

You need to be able to make friction work in your favour.

ACTIVITY 12

Sprinkle some salt on the table and then try sliding the heavy book (used in Activity 10) across the table.

1   Did the salt make the book easier or more difficult to move? (You may need to try Activity 10 again.)

2   Explain why:

Now turn over.

When you sprinkled salt on the table, you should have found that the book slid more easily – this is because the salt granules roll between the two surfaces. The rolling salt peels away from the table surface relatively easily, whereas the motion of two larger sliding surfaces is resisted by the greater number of bumps and grooves.

Dust and dirt have the same effect as the salt on squash courts and gym floors making them slippery and dangerous. This is why outdoor shoes (even those that look clean) should never be worn on these surfaces. Think about the relevance of frictional forces in your sport.

Dust and dirt on indoor sports surfaces makes them slippery and dangerous.

ACTIVITY 13

1 Describe activities/situations in your sport where the performer tries to reduce friction. If this is not applicable, use another sport. You may wish to refer back to the examples in Section 2.3.

- Sport:

- Situation:

- Describe how friction is reduced:

2 Describe activities/situations in your sport where the performer tries to increase friction. If this is not applicable, use another sport and refer back if you wish.

- Sport:

- Situation:

- Describe how friction is increased:

Now turn over.

1 *If your sport uses oil or grease in the mechanical parts of bikes, cars or equipment, you should have recognised these as ways of reducing friction. The oil or grease works rather like the salt, enabling surfaces to roll over each other. If your sport involves sliding or slipping, you should have noticed that smoothing the ice (as in ice skating and curling), or applying wax to the skis (as in downhill racing) reduces friction.*

2 *If your sport uses rigid shoes, studs or spikes, you should have suggested that the type of footwear was designed to increase friction. If it is important to maintain a good grip on equipment (eg racket, stick or bat; gymnastics apparatus; javelin and pole vault), you should have noted the use of special grips, gloves and even sticky hand resin to increase the friction between the performer's hand and the implement. Performers in these sports often suffer from blisters or develop callouses, which are two of the body's ways of protecting itself from friction.*

You are probably aware of other forces which slow objects down, for example air resistance.

Spiked shoes increase friction.

Use of oil reduces friction.

Applying wax to the skis reduces friction and helps the skier travel faster.

2.4 Air Resistance

Air resistance opposes the motion of objects through the air. Like friction, it is a force that always tends to slow objects down. As you free-wheel downhill on a bicycle or run into a head wind, you will feel the wind pressing against you, tending to slow you down. This effect is even greater if you wear baggy clothing, like a large sweatshirt or a waterproof cagoule. The effects of air resistance will be dealt with in detail in Chapter Six. For now it will be enough for you to remember that it slows things down as they try to travel through the air.

All the forces you have considered so far are examples of **external forces.** This means that they come from outside the objects or performers on which they act. In other words the:

- gravitational force pulling the cricket ball towards the ground originates outside the cricket ball

- frictional force slowing the skier originates outside the skier's body

- air resistance slowing the runner originates outside the runner's body.

An external force is necessary to move an object from place to place. An external force is also necessary to change the velocity[1] with which an object is moving. These are two important points which will be considered later in the pack.

In contrast, **internal forces** are those present inside the object or performer. Muscular forces are internal forces. Internal forces can change the shape of a body but on their own they cannot cause a body to move from one place to another.

2.5 Muscular Forces

The last force you need to consider is muscular force. This is the force over which you have the greatest control. You can decide where, when and how much force to apply, and the appropriateness of these decisions has an enormous effect on performance.

 How then do performers run, jump, leap and swim when they can only create internal forces?

The next activity should help to make things a little clearer.

---

1   **Velocity** is the speed and direction of a body. Velocity is measured in metres per second (m/s).
    Acceleration is measured in metres per second per second (m/s/s) and may also be expressed as metres per second squared (ms^{-2}).
    Add these to your own glossary.

ACTIVITY 14

1 Stand up and bend your elbows so that your hands are in front of your shoulders, palms facing forward. Now extend your arms forwards as if you were pushing someone away from you. Describe what happens:

2 Now stand facing a wall and repeat the exercise. Stand close enough to make good contact with the wall when you extend your arms forwards. Describe what happens:

Now turn over.

1 *No matter how vigorously you pushed, nothing much would have happened.*

2 *You should have found that you toppled backwards as a result of the push. By pushing against the wall, you brought into effect an external force.*

What actually happens is that as you push, the wall delivers a reaction force that acts on you. This reaction force acts on you from outside your body – it is an external force. The reaction force is delivered at exactly the same time as the push you exert on the wall – it is concurrent. It is also exactly the same size as the force you exert on the wall, but acts in the opposite direction (Figure 2).

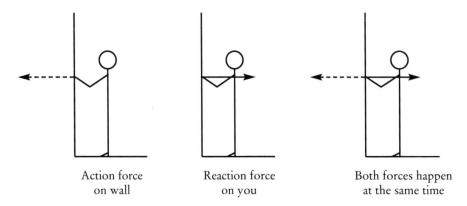

Action force on wall   Reaction force on you   Both forces happen at the same time

Figure 2: Action force and reaction force

This phenomenon was recognised by Sir Isaac Newton and became his third law of motion:

• For every force that is exerted by one body on another, there is a concurrent force, equal in size but opposite in direction exerted by the second body on the first.

It has become customary to call one of the forces the **action** force and the other the **reaction** force, although there is no agreement on which is which, and how they may be distinguished. Newton's third law is often called the action/reaction law and quoted in a much simpler form:

• For every action, there is an equal and opposite reaction.

This is useful as a reminder but it is important to realise that there is an action **force** and a reaction **force.** These forces:

• happen at the same time

• act in opposite directions

• are equal in size.

Newton's law also answers the question posed on Page 34:

• How do performers run, jump, leap and swim?

You know that external forces are needed to move an object or performer from place to place. You also know that performers can only generate internal, muscular forces.

Newton's third law shows that if you create internal muscular forces, you can exert these against objects. The reaction force is the external force that moves you. In simple terms, you need to push against something to move yourself from place to place.

This law is effective in sport over and over again. Newton's law can also help you understand the direction in which you need to push in order to go where you want to go. For example, to jump **up** you must push **down,** to jump **up and forward** you must push **down and back.**

You have now considered the major forces that are likely to influence any sporting situation:

- Gravity.
- Friction.
- Air resistance.
- Muscular forces.

In any situation, a combination of these forces will influence the movements of the object and/or the performers. The effect that is produced depends on the interaction of all the forces involved.

2.6 What Can a Force Do?

Before you look at some of the factors that affect outcome, think about what forces can do.

ACTIVITY 15

Think back (do not look back) to the first chapter and, in the left-hand column, jot down all the things that a force can do. In the right-hand column write an example of each (from your sport where possible):

A Force Can:	Examples

Now turn over.

Now look at the following list and see how many you wrote down. If necessary, add an example from your sport for each one listed:

A force can:

- *move an object*
  (eg the force from a bow that starts the arrow moving, the gravitational force that pulls the springboard diver downwards, the muscular force from a player that starts the football moving)
  Example:

- *stop an object moving*
  (eg the force from the floor that stops gymnasts when they land)
  Example:

- *change the direction in which an object is moving*
  (eg the force from the racket that sends the ball back over the net in a volley)
  Example:

- *change the speed at which an object is moving*
  (eg the extra muscular force that distance runners exert when they stride away from the pack, or the frictional force between the brakes and wheel that slows cyclists down)
  Example:

- *balance another force to keep an object still*
  (eg like the forces produced by two stationary tug of war teams)
  Example:

- *balance another force to keep an object moving at a steady speed*
  (eg the forces produced by a racing car travelling at constant velocity that balance the forces of friction and air resistance)
  Example:

- *change an object's shape*
  (eg the force of the trampolinist that stretches the springs).
  Example:

Being able to apply forces effectively helps the performer to be successful. Some performers seem to be able to do these things instinctively, while others struggle without success.

 What makes the difference?

A full analysis of all the forces involved would be a complicated and time-consuming task. There are three factors worthy of a closer look:

- Where the force is applied.
- In what direction the force is applied.
- How much force is applied.

Each one will be considered in turn.

Kick the ball this way.

The Point of Force Application

The next activity will help to show what happens when you change the point at which the force is applied.

ACTIVITY 16

For this activity, you will need a football (or a reasonably large ball). It is important to try to kick the ball in the same way each time and write down what happens. Try kicking different parts of the ball. Gently toe punt the ball:

- at the top:

    What happened?

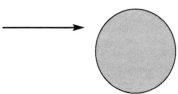

- near the middle:

    What happened?

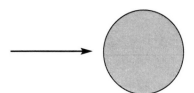

- at the bottom:

    What happened?

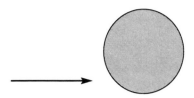

Now turn over.

You will have found that kicking:

- *near the top of the ball, made it roll slowly forward*
- *near the bottom of the ball, may have made it spin backwards*
- *near the middle of the ball, would have made it travel the greatest distance forward.*

In sports mechanics, the place where a force acts is called the **point of force application**. Where forces are applied through contact, the point of application is the point of contact between the two objects. In practice you are more likely to see an area of the force application, since there will be an area of contact between these two objects. For convenience and simplicity, it is assumed that the forces applied over the entire area can be represented by one force acting at the centre of this area (see Figure 3)

In kicking a football, the point of force application is shown by the asterisk *

Figure 3: The point of force application

Identifying the point of force application is quite straightforward in situations where objects are hit, pushed or lifted, or where the performer jumps, lands or runs. The next section explains where the point of force application is for gravity, air resistance and friction.

Point of Application of Gravitational Force

Gravitational force acts on each particle of matter in a body. It would be too complicated to represent each individual force, so the total effect of gravity on a body is shown by one force that acts at the body's centre of gravity. Figure 4 shows the gravitational force acting on a cricket ball falling through the air.

Figure 4: The point of application of gravitational force

The position of the centre of gravity is of particular importance in maintaining balance. This will be looked at in much greater detail in the next chapter.

Point of Application of Force of Air Resistance

Although it is known that air presses against the entire surface of a falling ball, it would also be too complicated to represent all the forces. Instead, the overall effect is represented with one force located in the centre of the surface facing the air resistance.

Figure 5 shows how the air resistance acting on a falling ball could be represented.

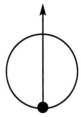

Figure 5: The point of application of air resistance

Point of Application of Force of Friction

Friction exists between the two surfaces that tend to slide or are sliding over one another. This situation can be simplified by representing the point of application of the force at the centre of the areas in contact (Figure 6).

Figure 6: The point of application of frictional force

Once you know where a force is applied, you can then begin to ask in what direction the force is being applied.

The Direction in Which Force is Applied

To produce motion in a straight line, the force must be directed through the centre of gravity of the object or performer. It must also be applied in the direction in which the object or performer needs to move. The term **centre of gravity** is explained in much greater detail in the next chapter. For now it is sufficient for you to think of the centre of gravity as an imaginary point roughly in the middle of any object.

For example, think of a volleyball player standing close to the net. The player needs to jump up to block a shot from the opposition without travelling forwards, for touching the net would mean losing the point. To do this, the player pushes down hard against the ground. A reaction force is created in response to this push. It is the same size and occurs at the same time as the action force, but it acts in the opposite direction – vertically upwards. As you can see from Figure 7, the reaction force is directed through the player's centre of gravity, and so the player moves upwards in a straight line.

Figure 7: Pushing down to jump up

Once the player is in the air, he can no longer push against the ground, so the only two forces acting are gravity and air resistance. In this situation the effect of air resistance is so small it can be ignored. As you know, gravity always pulls objects downwards towards the Earth, so from the moment the player becomes airborne, he starts to slow down. For a brief moment at the top of the jump, the player is stationary and then travels downwards, getting faster until reaching the ground. Since gravity also acts through the player's centre of gravity, it also produces movement in a straight line.

This sort of movement is an example of linear motion (motion in a line). Since the volleyball player travels up and down in a straight line, the motion is described as **rectilinear.**

Now think of a soccer goalkeeper, jumping forwards and upwards to punch away a ball crossing in front of the goal (Figure 8). The keeper needs to push downwards (to create an upward reaction force) and backwards (to create a forward reaction force) to travel in the right direction. Notice how he rocks forward slightly so the reaction force is still directed through the centre of gravity. This sort of movement is also an example of linear motion. However, because all parts of the keeper's body follow the same curved pathway, the motion is described as **curvilinear.**

Figure 8: Pushing down and back to jump up and forward

It may be helpful to think about the total force as a combination of vertical and horizontal forces. If the goalkeeper missed the ball because the jump was too low, more downward force was needed to produce a greater upward reaction force. If the jump was high enough but too short, the keeper needed to push harder backwards to create a greater forward reaction force.

A more precise and mathematical version of this technique involves the use of **vector diagrams** (special diagrams that represent forces). Go back and look at Figures 2–8. In these diagrams, the arrows represent forces. If you are interested in finding out more about vectors, read Panel E over the page.

Panel E: Vectors

Vectors are lines whose length and direction are used to represent some quantity, such as force, velocity or acceleration. When vectors are used to represent forces, the:

- size of the force is represented by the length of the line so in accurate representations a scale is also needed (eg 1cm – 1N)

- direction in which the force acts is indicated by the direction of the line and arrow head

- point of application of force is indicated by the position of the tail of the arrow.

The sum of two or more vectors is called the resultant. The resultant of two vectors can be found by completing the parallelogram with the two vectors as sides (Figure 9).

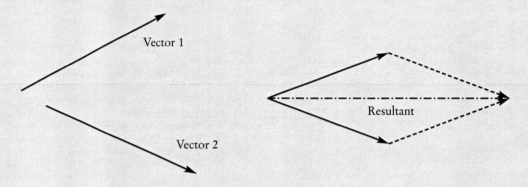

Figure 9: The parallelogram of forces

Sometimes the resultant is known but the horizontal and vertical components need to be calculated. This is done by drawing a parallelogram with the resultant as the diagonal (Figure 10).

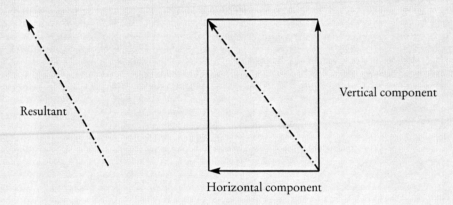

Figure 10: Parallelogram of forces

The resultant of two or more vectors can be found by placing the vectors head to tail, maintaining their lengths and directions. The resultant is the vector drawn from the tail of the first arrow to the head of the last arrow (Figure 11).

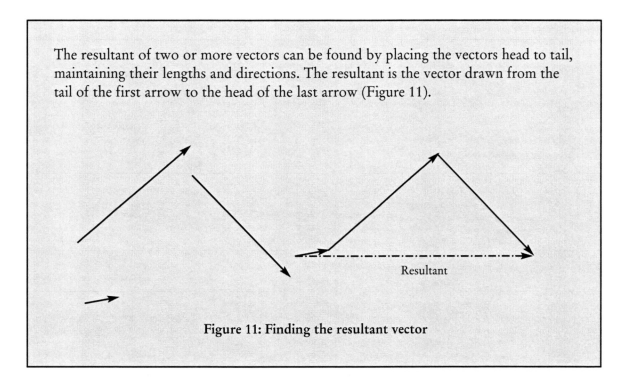

Figure 11: Finding the resultant vector

If the force is not directed through the centre of gravity, rotation will occur. This is what happens to make a tennis ball spin or a diver somersault. This will be dealt with in more detail in Chapter Five.

How good are you at recognising the point at which a force acts? Test yourself with the activity over the page.

ACTIVITY 17

Draw an arrow to represent the named forces for each diagram below:

1 Hockey ball being hit (force of impact from stick):

Figure 12a: Striking a hockey ball

2 Basketball shot (force from right hand):

Figure 13a: Basketball shot

3 Skier sliding downhill (friction):

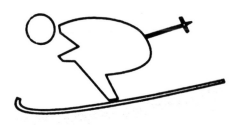

Figure 14a: Skiing downhill

4   Runner (air resistance):

Figure 15a: Running into a head wind

5   Diver being propelled upwards by the springboard (force from board):

Figure 16a: Diving from the board

Now turn over.

Check your answers by comparing your diagrams with the following. Pay particular attention to the position of the tail of the arrow.

1 *Hockey ball being hit (force of impact from stick):*

Figure 12b: Striking a hockey ball

2 *Basketball shot (force from right hand):*

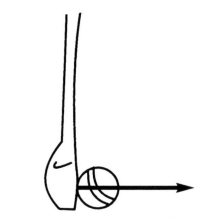

Figure 13b: Basketball shot

3 *Skier sliding downhill (friction):*

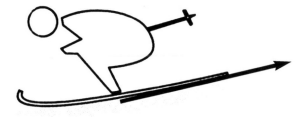

Figure 14b: Skiing downhill

4 *Runner (air resistance):*

Figure 15b: Running into a head wind

5 *Diver being propelled upwards by the springboard (force from board):*

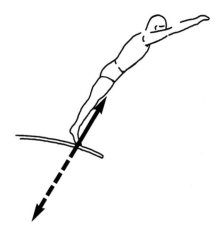

Figure 16b: Diving from the board

If your diagrams were similar to Figures 12b to 16b, then you are ready to go on. If you made several mistakes or are still uncertain about the point of force application, finish reading this paragraph and then go back over the section. If you are still uncertain after rereading the section, do not worry. Leave it for a while and try following up some of the references listed at the end of this chapter before trying these exercises again. Alternatively it might be helpful to talk to an experienced coach or sport scientist.

The Size of the Force

The final factor to be considered is the size of the force. There are two principles to remember about the size of the force applied to an object:

- For a constant mass, the acceleration produced is directly proportional to the force applied.

- The greater the mass, the greater the force required to produce a given acceleration.

The first point confirms what you will intuitively know from everyday experience, that the harder you push an object, the faster it will travel. For example, you know that the harder you push a door, the faster it will slam shut; the harder you kick a ball, the faster it will travel. **Directly proportional** means that if you double the amount of force applied to an object, the acceleration produced will also be doubled. The second point is explained in more detail in the remainder of this section.

The harder you push an object, the faster it will travel.

ACTIVITY 18

Imagine a dumb-bell and a baseball are in separate cardboard boxes on the ground. You must slide both boxes along the ground (Figure 17).

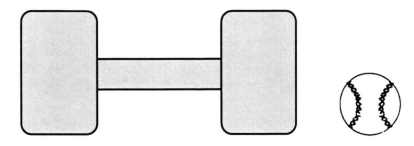

Figure 17: Some objects have a greater resistance to motion than others

Explain which you think would be more difficult to get moving:

Now turn over.

The dumb-bell would be harder to get moving because it has the greater mass, and so a greater resistance to motion. This resistance to motion is called **inertia.**

Having read about friction earlier in this chapter, you might reasonably conclude that the dumb-bell is more difficult to get moving because it is heavier and hence a greater frictional force is generated which opposes its motion.

The difference in frictional force does not entirely account for the differences in how difficult it is to get the two objects moving. If you were to suspend each object by a thread, the dumb-bell would still be the more difficult to get moving. Try this out for yourself in Activity 19 using a very heavy book (your equivalent to the dumb-bell) and a light book (equivalent to the baseball).

Some objects have a greater resistance to motion than others.

ACTIVITY 19

1   Try pushing the large heavy book and then the small light book along the table. Which one is harder to get moving?

2   Now place each book in a carrier bag. Ask a friend to take one carrier bag in each hand and hold both out in front of him. Now try to get each one moving again. Explain what happens:

Now turn over.

You should still have felt a difference in how hard it is to get the books moving. The important thing to realise is that the more massive the object, the more force is required to get it moving.

If you wish to study the law which explains this, read panel F.

Panel F: The Law of Acceleration

Newton's second law, the **law of acceleration**, describes how the rate of change of momentum is proportional to the applied force and takes place in the direction in which the force is applied. Where the mass (m) remains constant, the acceleration produced (a) is proportional to the applied force (F) and takes place in the direction in which the force is applied. This can be expressed as an equation:

$$F = ma$$

 What are the implications for performers and coaches?

An overweight performer will have to generate extra force to move his surplus body mass. Consequently the overweight performer might be expected to tire more quickly than the performer of an appropriate weight. This may be particularly important in events where the performer is active for a long period of time, such as the marathon, when the cumulative effect of fatigue can be considerable.

In some sports, especially gymnastics, it is an advantage to be very light and coaches often speak of their gymnasts having a favourable strength to weight ratio (ie being strong but light). This means that the resistance to motion is relatively small.

However, in some instances there is some advantage to be gained from being more massive than the opponent. Additional mass is useful (eg in resisting shoulder charges in football or in a hand off in rugby). In these situations, the additional mass makes the player more difficult to stop or knock over.

Some sports require very little movement and being massive may be more important than being mobile. Examples might be in sumo wrestling and tug of war competitions.

You are now very close to the end of this chapter on forces, and you should have picked up several pieces of the biomechanics jigsaw. You should know which forces are important to sportspeople and what sorts of effects can be produced. The last section will have helped you to understand the three factors that contribute to the successful application of these forces. In the next section, you will see how all these fragments of information can fit together to give you a simple framework for analysing sports situations that involve linear motion.

2.7 Recap and Key Points

If it involves **analysing linear motion**, think about:

- what forces are involved

- where the point of application of the force is

- in what direction the force acts (force must be applied through the object's centre of gravity to produce linear motion)

- how much force is being applied.

To check your understanding of the concepts described in this chapter, try the self tester over the page.

SELF TESTER FOR CHAPTER TWO

1 What is meant by the word **force**:

2 List the forces that are important to movement in sport:

-
-
-
-

3 List seven things that a force can do and give an example of each.

A Force Can:	Examples
1	
2	
3	
4	
5	
6	
7	

4 Complete the following sentence:

An _____ force is necessary to _____ an object from
place to place. An _____ force is also necessary to change the _____
with which an object is moving. In contrast _____ forces are those that are
present _____ the object or performer. _____ forces can change the shape
of a body but on their own cannot cause a body to move from place to place.
Gravity, air resistance and friction are all _____ forces. Muscular forces are
_____ forces.

5   Name two different sorts of friction:

    •

    •

6   Give one example of how friction is reduced, and one example of how friction is increased in your sport (choose another sport if yours is unsuitable).

    •   Friction is reduced by:

    •   Friction is increased by:

7   What features of force can be represented by arrows?

8   What is inertia?

Now turn over.

1 *What is meant by the word force?*

   Check your answer with the dictionary explanation in Activity 7 (Page 15) and compare it to the definitions given on Page 16.

2 *List the forces that are important to movement in sport:*

   - *Gravitational force.*

   - *Frictional force.*

   - *Air resistance.*

   - *Muscular forces.*

3 *List seven things that a force can do and give an example of each:*

   A force can:

   - *start an object moving*

   - *stop an object moving*

   - *change the direction in which an object is moving*

   - *change the speed at which it is moving*

   - *balance another force to keep an object still*

   - *balance another force to keep an object moving at a steady speed*

   - *change an object's shape.*

   The examples provided on Pages 36 and 37 may help you check your own examples. If you are still not sure whether your answers are correct, discuss your ideas with a senior coach or a sports scientist.

4 *Complete the following sentence:*

   *An **external** force is necessary to **move** an object from place to place. An **external** force is also necessary to change the **velocity** with which an object is moving. In contrast **internal** forces are those that are present **inside** the object or performer. **Internal** forces can change the shape of a body but on their own cannot cause a body to move from place to place. Gravity, air resistance and friction are all **muscular** forces. Muscular forces are **external** forces.*

5 *Name two different sorts of friction:*

   - *Static friction is the friction that prevents two surfaces from slipping over each other.*

   - *Dynamic friction resists the motion of two surfaces that are sliding over each other.*

6   *Give one example of how friction is reduced, and one example of how friction is increased in your sport (choose another sport if yours is unsuitable):*

Use the examples on Pages 31–33 to help check your answers. If you are still unsure, consult a senior experienced coach in your sport or a sports scientist.

7   *What features of force can be represented by arrows?*

- *The size of the force is represented by the length of the arrow.*
- *The point of application of the force is indicated by the position of the tail of the arrow.*
- *The direction in which the force acts is shown by the direction of the arrow.*

8   *What is inertia?*

Inertia is a measure of an object's reluctance to move or to change its linear motion. Inertia is related to mass – the greater the mass of an object the greater its inertia.

If you had any difficulty with this self tester, go back and reread the relevant parts before moving on to the next chapter.

2.8 Further Help

Bartlett, RM (1997) **Introduction to sports biomechanics.**
London, E & FN Spon. ISBN 0-4192-08402.
Chapter 2: Movement (kinematic) Considerations (pp47–69)
and Chapter 3: Linear and Angular Kinetics (pp82–99).

Daish, CB (1972) **Physics of ball games.**
London, English Universities Press. ISBN 0-3400-53992.

Dick, FW (1989) **Sports training principles.**
2nd edition. London, A & C Black. ISBN 0-7136-5644-1.

Dyson, GHG (1986) **Dyson's mechanics of athletics.**
8th edition. London, Hodder and Stoughton Educational. ISBN 0-340-39172-3.
Chapter 2: Motion (pp4–13) and Chapter 4: Forces (pp24–60).

Hall, S (1991) **Basic biomechanics.** St Louis MS, Mosby. ISBN 0-8016-2087-2.
Chapter 9: Movement Linear Kinematics (pp252–287) and Chapter 11: The use of
force (pp316–349).

Hay, JG (1993) **The biomechanics of sports techniques.**
4th edition. London, Prentice Hall. ISBN 0-13-084534-5.
Chapter 2: Forms of motion (pp8–12), Chapter 3: Linear Kinematics (pp 13–46),
and Chapter 5: Linear Kinetics (pp60–110).

Kreighbaum, E and Barthels, KM (1985) **Biomechanics: a qualitative approach for
studying human movement** 2nd edition. New York, Macmillan. ISBN 0-02-366-480-0.
Chapter 2: Fundamental mechanical concepts and Chapter 3: Forces and human
motion.

Maintaining and Losing Balance (Stability)

3.0 Introduction

People often talk about good balance in sport – not just in gymnastics, where the ability to maintain a position is an inherent feature of the activity. Balance is important in a whole range of sports – the balanced runner, the balanced stance of the shooter, the balanced position of the receiver in tennis, the wide, low and stable stance of the judo player and so on.

People also speak of being off-balance. Often this is used in a derogatory way – the fencer was caught off-balance, the scrum half was off-balance and gave a poor pass. Being able to put an opponent off-balance can be a useful skill to acquire. In tennis, this is referred to as wrong-footing an opponent – making them go the wrong way, so they are unable to move quickly in the right direction.

Being nearly off-balance can also be a valuable quality. It is useful to be nearly off-balance if you want to be able to move rapidly in a particular direction – for example, the netball player at the centre pass, the sprinter off the blocks, the tennis player following a serve into the net.

Often sportspeople learn quite naturally to use balance and off-balance to their advantage – they do it without thinking. If you want to analyse performance in detail (eg to improve performance), it is valuable to take a closer look at the principles which underlie stability and instability. In this chapter, you will be introduced to a number of factors which influence stability – mass, centre of gravity, line of gravity and base of support. Do not worry, they are all quite straightforward and you will find that you are probably familiar with them already, even though you may not have heard of their technical terms.

By the end of this chapter, you should be able to:

- explain the terms centre of gravity, line of gravity and base of support
- draw diagrams to show the relationship between centre of gravity, line of gravity and base of support for a performer executing a technique in your sport
- state the four factors that affect stability
- identify situations in your sport in which the principles of stability (or instability) can influence the effectiveness of a technique
- modify techniques in your sport to achieve the required degree of stability.

In everyday language, terms such as stability, equilibrium and balance are often used interchangeably. In mechanics they mean different things, so first you need to check their exact meaning. You may wish to add these to your own glossary.

Equilibrium

Objects or people are in a state of equilibrium when their motion is not changing. There are two types of equilibrium:

- Static equilibrium – used to describe a stationary object or person.
- Dynamic equilibrium – used to describe an object or person travelling with constant velocity (at the same speed in the same direction).

Stability

This term describes how difficult it is to disturb the equilibrium of an object or person. For example, a stable stationary object would be difficult to tip over. A stable moving object would be difficult to slow down or speed up, or move in a different direction.

Balance

This word is used to describe the process of controlling equilibrium. For example, a gymnast trying to balance in a handstand is trying to achieve and maintain static equilibrium; a cyclist trying to balance round a tight corner is trying to maintain dynamic equilibrium.

This chapter deals mainly with stability – what makes an object or person difficult to knock over, or resistant to changes in its motion. The idea of stability was covered briefly in the Introductory Study Pack *Improving Techniques*. In this chapter, the idea will be explained in mechanical terms. Although the basic ideas may be familiar, you may be introduced to some new concepts. Understanding the principles of stability should help you to develop a framework for analysing and therefore improving performance.

3.1 Stability

Start trying to work out some of the basic principles for yourself by working through the following activity with a partner.

ACTIVITY 20

1   Push your partner from one side, then from behind and then from in front. Ask your partner not to move his/her feet. Each time, watch your partner carefully and write down what happened when you pushed from:

- the side:

- behind:

- in front:

2   This time, tell your partner to move his/her feet to try to resist being moved. Notice what your partner does and how successful he/she was in staying still. Write down your observations. Try to explain what made your partner more stable when you pushed from:

- the side:

- behind:

- in front:

Continued...

3   Ask your partner to stand with feet apart. Tell your partner which direction you are
    going to push and ask him/her to resist being moved. Note what happened when
    you pushed from:

    • the side:

    • behind:

Tell your partner which direction you are going to push.

4 Try to write down any principles that you noticed which seemed to influence your partner's stability. Some headings are provided to help you:

- size of base:

- size of base in relation to the direction of force (push):

- distribution of weight over the base:

- stance of the person (eg how high, how low):

Now turn over.

You will probably have noticed that it was more difficult to move your partner when she held a wide base of support (eg feet apart). To be effective, this needed to be wide in a particular direction. In other words, if you wanted to resist a push from the side, the base needed to be wide from side to side (ie feet apart, not one forward and one back – Figure 18a). On the other hand, if the push was coming from behind, it is better to have a wide base made by having one foot forward and one foot back (Figure 18b).

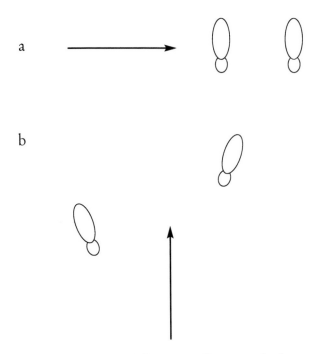

Figure 18: Changing the base to resist a push

You may also have noticed that your partner found it easier to resist a push if the knees were bent. Keeping the body low makes people more stable (think about the judo player, the combat sportsmen).

Your partner may have leaned towards you in anticipation of the push . Think of the rugby player preparing to block the impact of another player moving towards him.

You may have managed to push your partner over completely. Think about why this happened.

You will have a chance to come back to check your ideas later and explain what you have found in mechanical terms. First you will need to pick up a few more pieces of the mechanics jigsaw – centre of gravity, base of support and line of gravity. The relationship between these three factors is of key importance in understanding the principles of stability.

3.2 Centre of Gravity

First you must clarify some terminology – mass and centre of gravity (Panel G).

Panel G: Mass and Centre of Gravity

Mass is the amount of matter a body possesses, the number of particles within an object.

The centre of gravity is an imaginary point. It is the point at which the body's weight can be considered to act. In a regular shaped object in which the mass is uniformly distributed (eg a football[1]), the centre of gravity would be found at the geometrical centre of that object. At this point, half the mass is above and half below, half the mass is in front and half is behind, half the mass is to the left and half to the right of the centre of gravity.

It is useful to identify the position of the centre of gravity when analysing a movement in sport. Although it is possible to measure this accurately[2], this is not always necessary when trying to improve sports performance. A good estimate by eye will be sufficient in many cases – this is what the coach has to rely on out on the field, in the gym or on court.

---

1   This is not completely accurate because there are some irregularities such as the valve and seams.

2   There are several scientific ways to determine the centre of gravity of various objects. If you are interested in finding out about these, there are some references at the end of this chapter.

Study the diagrams below. The centre of gravity of these blocks is marked by the dot.

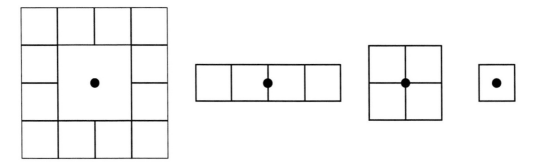

NB It is possible for the centre of gravity to be located outside the object.

Figure 19: The approximate position of the centre of gravity

The next activity will help you to check your understanding of this concept.

ACTIVITY 21

1 In Figure 20a, the dot marks the centre of gravity of the pile of blocks. Three of the dots are in the right place. Place a circle around the diagram which is wrong:

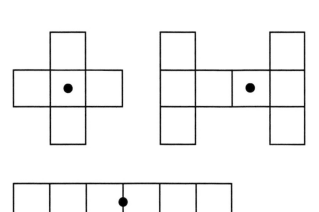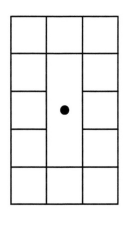

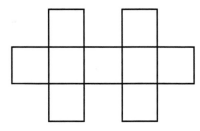

Figure 20a: Centre of gravity of blocks

2 Estimate the position of the centre of gravity of the blocks below:

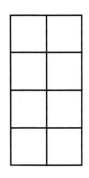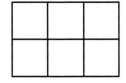

Figure 21a: Locating centre of gravity

Now turn over.

You will probably have found this quite straightforward. Check your diagrams with the following:

1

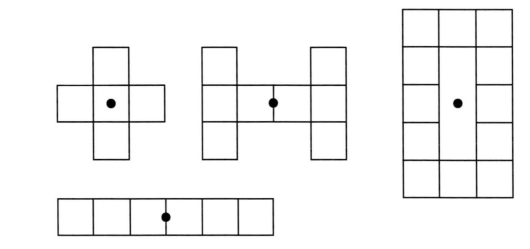

Figure 20b: Corrected centre of gravity

2

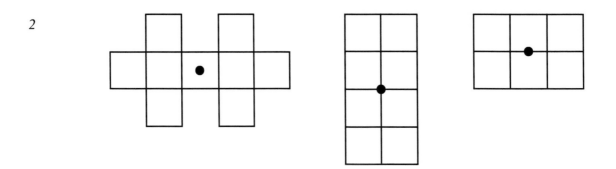

Figure 21b: Correctly located centre of gravity

So far, locating the centre of gravity has been easy because the objects (and the groups of objects) have been of a regular shape, and the mass evenly distributed within the objects. What happens if the objects are the same size and shape but some objects in the group contain different amounts of mass (different densities)? See Panel H for more information.

Panel H: Density

The **density** of an object is its mass per unit volume; in other words, the amount of matter packed into a given space.

A broom handle is much less dense than an iron bar of the same dimensions. If you could count the number of particles of matter inside the broom handle and the iron bar, you would find a much larger number of particles in the iron bar.

In Chapter Two, it was pointed out that gravity exerts a force on each particle of matter within a body, pulling each one towards the ground. The combined effect of all these tiny forces is called the body's weight – the more particles in an object, the larger its weight. This explains why the iron bar is heavier than the broom handle.

What happens to the centre of gravity if some blocks are more dense than others? Imagine the dark blocks in Figure 22 below are filled with a dense substance (for example lead), while the light boxes are filled with a less dense substance such as air.

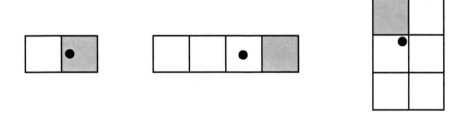

Figure 22: Estimating location of the centre of gravity when the density varies

Notice how the position of the centre of gravity (shown by the dot) moves towards the dense blocks.

In sport situations you often have to deal with objects whose mass is unevenly distributed. Many objects also have irregular shapes, which makes things more complicated.

ACTIVITY 22

Look around the room and list five irregular shaped objects in which density varies (ie mass is unevenly distributed):

-

-

-

-

-

You will have found that many objects fit this description. Did you include the human body in your list? Understanding about the centre of gravity of the body is very important for anyone studying sports performance.

 Where is the centre of gravity of the human body?

The body is made up of a variety of different materials of different densities[1]. Muscles are more dense than bone; muscle, bone and body fluids are all relatively high density materials in comparison to fat and air.

When you stand up with your arms by your side, your centre of gravity lies just below the navel, about midway between the front and back of the body (Figure 23).

The position of the centre of gravity alters as you change position. If you lift your arms above your head, the centre of gravity moves slightly upwards (Figure 24).

Figure 23: The location of the centre of gravity in a performer

Figure 24: The position of the centre of gravity with arms lifted

1   If you are unfamiliar with the structure of the body, you are recommended to read the NCF home study pack *An Introduction to the Structure of the Body*, available from Coachwise Ltd (0113 231 1310).

The arms represent about 11% of the body mass, a fairly small proportion of the total, so moving them only has a small effect on the position of the centre of gravity. If a larger part of the body is moved (eg the trunk, which constitutes about 50% of total body mass), the shift in the centre of gravity will be more marked. For example, if you lean forward in a pike position (Figure 25), the centre of gravity is moved outside the body.

If you lift up a heavy object, the centre of gravity shifts – the heavier the object, the greater the effect (Figure 26).

Figure 25: The position of the centre of gravity when the body is piked

Figure 26: The centre of gravity moves when a heavy object is carried

ACTIVITY 23

Mark the location of the centre of gravity on the diagrams below:

Figure 27a: The centre of gravity in various sports figures

Now turn over.

Check your diagrams with those shown below:

Figure 27b: The centre of gravity in various sports figures

Being able to identify the position of the centre of gravity is useful in analysing sports performance. Remember this is just one piece of the jigsaw that you need in order to understand stability. The next piece to consider is the base of support.

3.3 Base of Support

You need to be able to recognise the base of support of a performer in order to analyse stability. Look at Panel I and then work through the diagrams.

Panel I: Base of Support

The base of support of an object is the area encompassed by the parts that touch the ground. In other words, when you are standing, the base of support is not simply the area covered by each foot, but includes the total area between the two feet. This is why in Activity 20 (Page 65) the size of the base could be increased by standing with feet apart or with one foot forward and one foot back (Figure 28).

Figure 28: The base of support

In the diagram below, the base of support of the performer standing on one foot is represented in two ways – with a bracket (left) and a floor plan (right).

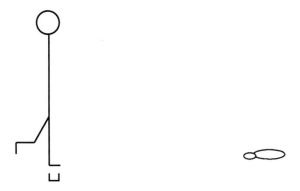

Figure 29: The base of support (one foot)

If the performer then puts both feet down, the base of support changes and looks like this:

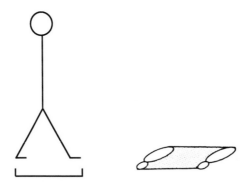

Figure 30: The base of support (two feet)

If the performer puts both hands down, the base of support can be shown like this:

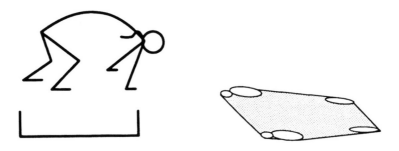

Figure 31: The base of support (two feet and two hands)

Check your understanding of the concept of base of support by working through the following activity.

The size of the base of support affects stability.

ACTIVITY 24

Draw in the base of support in the following diagrams – show it as a bracket and then as a floor plan.

Figure 32a: Base of support in various sports figures

Now turn over.

Check your drawings with those given below:

Figure 32b: Base of support in various sports figures

Now you can locate the centre of gravity and identify the base of support of a performer. One more piece of the jigsaw must be explained before you can understand the factors that influence the stability of the performer.

3.4 Line of Gravity

This is quite simply a line extending from the centre of gravity vertically down to the ground.

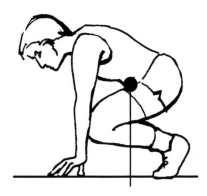

Figure 33: The line of gravity

ACTIVITY 25

Add the line of gravity on the diagrams below:

Gymnast

Runner

Figure 34a: Line of gravity

Now turn over.

Check your drawings with those given below:

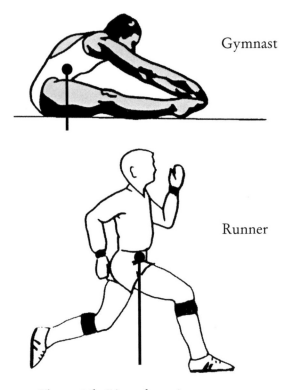

Gymnast

Runner

Figure 34b: Line of gravity

Now you need to consider these three principles at the same time and work out how they influence the stability of the sports performer in action.

ACTIVITY 26

1 Look at the following diagram of a performer. The centre of gravity, line of gravity
   and floor plan have been marked. The cross on the floor plan shows where the line
   of gravity would land on the floor plan.

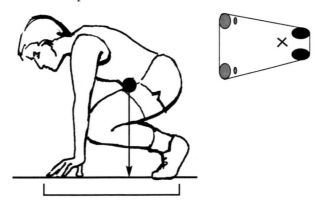

Figure 35: Finding out where the line of gravity intersects the floor plan

Continued...

2 Check your understanding by filling in the missing parts in the following diagrams. Each diagram should have a centre of gravity, line of gravity, base of support, intersect point of line of gravity on floor plan. State whether each position is stable or unstable.

Figure 36: Analysing the position of the centre of gravity and where the line of gravity intersects the floor plan

3 Write down the factors that you think influence a person's stability:

-

-

-

-

Now turn over.

There are four factors that affect a body's stability:

- *The size of the base of support.*
  The bigger the base of support, the more stable the object. You are more stable standing on two feet than one. For example, a boxer increases the size of his base by moving his feet further apart.

- *The height of the centre of gravity above the base of support.*
  The lower the centre of gravity, the more stable the object. For example, the judo player gets lower to make it more difficult to be thrown.

- *The distance of the line of centre of gravity from the edge of the base of support.*
  The greater the distance, the more stable the performer. For all round stability it is best to have the line of centre of gravity falling over the centre of the base. Athletes in the sprint start position are very stable in the initial crouch position but very unstable in the ready position. This occurs because the line of the centre of gravity falls so close to the front edge of the base. The slightest push results in them moving forwards and out of the blocks. If the centre of gravity is too far back, the effectiveness of the start is reduced; if the line of gravity falls outside the base, they would topple forward. Try making the sprint start shape and feel how much weight you bear on your fingers. It would only take a small push to make you topple forwards.

- *The mass of the body.*
  The greater the mass, the more stable the object. It is more difficult to push over a rugby forward than a jockey. This is important to remember in certain situations (eg during the adolescent growth spurt) and in certain sports (eg weightlifting, the combat sports in which there are weight categories, and contact sports).

In Part 2 of the previous activity, the positions shown in Diagrams a, b and c are unstable and those shown in Diagrams d and e are stable.

These four principles apply both in situations where the performer is moving and in situations where the performer is still[1]. They also provide a framework for analysing balance related activities in sport which are summarised in the next section.

---

1   This chapter has dealt almost exclusively with activities where the performer is still, or trying to resist motion. The references at the end of this chapter provide information on how to apply these principles to situations where the performer is moving.

This chapter has looked at a number of factors which influence stability and instability. These factors, and their relationship between each other, is summarised in the next section.

3.5 Recap and Key Points

If it involves **analysing stability**, think about the:

- size of the base
- height of the centre of gravity
- position of the line of gravity
- mass.

Factors	To be Unstable	To be Stable
Size of Base	As small as possible	As large as possible
Height of Centre of Gravity	As high as possible	As low as possible
Position of Line of Gravity	Near edge of the base	Far from edge of base
Mass	As little as possible	As big as possible

To check your understanding of the concepts described in this chapter, try the self tester over the page.

SELF TESTER FOR CHAPTER THREE

1 Give a brief explanation of each of the following terms, using a diagram where necessary:

- Centre of gravity:

- Line of gravity:

- Base of support:

2 Think of a situation in your sport where the performer needs to be unstable. Draw a stick figure to show the position of the performer:

Add:

- a dot to show the position of the performer's centre of gravity

- the line of gravity

- a floor plan

- a cross on the floor plan to show where the line of gravity intersects it.

Explain what makes this an unstable position:

3   Explain how the performer in Question 2 could become less stable:

4   Repeat Question 2, this time selecting a situation from your sport where the performer needs to be very stable:

Explain what makes this a stable position:

5   Explain how the performer in Question 4 could become more stable:

6   List the four factors that affect a body's stability:

-
-
-
-

Now turn over.

1 *Give a brief explanation of each of the following terms:*

- *Centre of gravity:*

The point at which the body's mass can be considered to act.

- *Line of gravity:*

A line extending from the object's centre of gravity vertically down to the ground.

- *Base of support:*

The area encompassed by the parts of the object that touch the ground.

2 *Think of a situation in your sport where the performer needs to be unstable. Draw a stick figure to show the position of the performer:*

Refer back to check whether you have correctly located the centre of gravity (Section 3.2), line of gravity (Section 3.4) and the point at which the line of gravity intersects the base of support (Section 3.4).

Some or all of the following points may contribute to making your example unstable:

- *A small base.*
- *The centre of gravity high above the base.*
- *The line of gravity near the edge of the base.*
- *The performer has a small mass.*

3 *Explain how the performer in Question 2 could become less stable:*

The performer could become less stable by:

- *reducing the size of the base*
- *increasing the height of the centre of gravity above the base*
- *moving the line of gravity closer to the edge of the base*
- *reducing their mass.*

4 *Repeat Question 2, this time selecting a situation from your sport where the performer needs to be very stable. Explain what makes this a stable position:*

Some or all of the following points may contribute to making your second example stable:

- *A large base.*
- *The centre of gravity low.*
- *The line of gravity far from the edge of the base.*
- *The performer has a large mass.*

You may also need the advice of an experienced coach in your sport.

5 *Explain how the performer in Question 2 could become more stable:*

The performer could become more stable by:

- *increasing the size of the base*
- *lowering the centre of gravity*
- *moving the line of gravity further from the edge of the base*
- *gaining mass.*

The adjustments you have suggested for your performer will be based on these principles, but you will need the advice of an experienced coach to check your suggestions.

6 *List the four factors that affect a body's stability:*

- *The size of the base.*
- *The height of the centre of gravity above the base.*
- *The distance of the line of gravity from the edge of the base.*
- *The mass of the object or performer.*

If you had any difficulty with this self tester, go back and reread the relevant parts before moving on to the next chapter.

3.6 Further Help

Bartlett, RM (1997) **Introduction to sports biomechanics.**
London, E&FN Spon. ISBN 0-4192-08402.
Chapter 6: Angular Kinetics (pp126-153).

Hall, S (1991) **Basic biomechanics.** St Louis MS, Mosby.
ISBN 0-8016-2087-2.
Chapter 12: Movement Equilibrium (pp350–388).

Hay, JG (1993) **The biomechanics of sports techniques.**
4th edition. London, Prentice Hall. ISBN 0-13-084534-5.

Starting and Stopping (Momentum and Impulse)

4.0 Introduction

Sport performers are often required to start and stop moving quickly, to change direction or pace. This is particularly true for games players – picture the rugby player, volleyball player or squash player in action. Moving off quickly is also important in other activities (eg cycling, running, swimming). In some activities, it is necessary to get an object moving (eg a javelin, a golf ball), stop an object (eg in catching) or redirect an object (eg hitting and striking activities).

For example, in cricket, the:

- fast bowler is trying to bowl as fast as possible, giving the ball momentum
- batsman is intercepting the ball in flight to try to change its momentum
- fielders are attempting to stop the ball and stop its momentum.

The changes that happen in sport can be categorised into three broad groups:

- Starting things moving.
- Stopping things moving.
- Changing the speed or direction in which an object is moving.

From Chapter Two, you know that force is necessary to produce a change in the way an object moves. Try Activity 27 over the page which analyses how forces make things move and stop.

ACTIVITY 27

The table below shows examples of how forces make things move and stop in two sports. Do the same for seven other sports (including your own):

Key:
x = not required
/ = required

Sport	Getting Things Moving						Making Things Stop			
	Push	Lift	Kick	Throw	Hit	Jump	Land	Catch	Trap	Brake
Tennis	x	x	x	/	/	/	/	x	/	/
Gymnastics	/	/	x	/	x	/	/	/	x	/

You will probably have found that almost every sport involves getting things moving or bringing things to a stop. Clearly, being able to get things moving is an important feature of many sports.

In sports with which you are familiar, you will probably be able to identify a particular performer who excels at each type of activity. Think of a:

- sprinter who has a particularly explosive start:

- footballer whose free kicks are hard and accurate:

- swimmer with a strong push from the wall after a turn:

- tennis player with a fast serve:

- basketball player with a powerful jump:

Being able to stop things moving is equally important in order to maintain control, avoid injury or successfully complete a technique. You will be able to picture:

- trapping or catching skills in sports such as football, cricket and netball
- slowing-down techniques needed by skiers, cyclists, javelin throwers or indoor sprinters
- efficient landing techniques needed by gymnasts, football goalkeepers, ski-jumpers, basketball players and long jumpers.

All these are important skills. What is it that makes one performer more successful than another? Why are some performers prone to injury? Try the next activity.

ACTIVITY 28

Write down six factors which determine how successfully the performer executes these actions:

-

-

-

-

-

-

Now turn over.

You will probably have thought of some of the following:

- Physical factors such as strength, flexibility, power, co-ordination.
- Psychological factors such as concentration, reaction time.
- Technical factors such as effectiveness of the technique, timing, level of skill.

Clearly it helps if you are naturally strong or have a particular body type that is ideally suited to an event. It will also be helpful if the performer can shut out distractions and concentrate on the task. However, regardless of the amount of natural talent, the really important factor is how effectively the performer is able to use this talent.

Two mechanical principles, momentum and impulse, are particularly relevant to the sorts of actions you have been considering. This chapter will look at these, apply them to sporting situations and help you identify what makes certain techniques more effective than others.

By the end of this chapter, you should be able to:

- explain what is meant by momentum
- describe the factors which affect the amount of momentum a body possesses
- explain what is meant by impulse
- describe ways to start and stop things moving more effectively
- apply these principles to your own sport and identify ways to improve technique.

4.1 What is Momentum?

Although momentum has a specific meaning to sports biomechanists, it is a word used in everyday language – especially by sports commentators. It is often used inaccurately to describe a wide range of situations, or applied inappropriately to abstract concepts such as ideas or tactical moves in sport. By the end of this section you should understand its true meaning. Start by tackling the next activity.

ACTIVITY 29

1 Two athletes, a powerful, heavy shot-putter and a slim long distance runner, are training out on the track. They stride down the finishing straight side by side. One athlete possesses more momentum than the other. Place a tick beside the athlete who has more momentum:

- The runner

- The shot-putter

Explain your answer:

2 Consider the two situations below and place a tick beside the one which you think has more momentum:

- A tennis ball served by a top tennis player

- A tennis ball thrown to a player by a ball boy/girl

Explain what gives one ball more momentum than the other.

3 Write down what you think is meant by momentum:

Now turn over.

Compare your answer with the explanation of momentum given in Panel J.

Panel J: Momentum

Momentum is a body's quantity of motion. This can be a difficult idea to grasp. It is often easier to remember that the amount of momentum a body has depends on how much mass the body has and how fast the body is travelling.

In the earlier examples, the long distance runner and shot-putter were running with the same velocity down the track, but the shot-putter had the greater momentum because he had a much larger mass than the long distance runner.

The two tennis balls have the same mass. The ball served by the top tennis player would have a much larger momentum because it would be travelling at high speed (often around 100 mph). In comparison the ball thrown by the ball girl would be travelling slowly.

The simple equation summarising the relationship between momentum (M), mass (m) and velocity (v) is:

$$M = mv$$

Momentum is equal to mass x velocity measured in kg m/s

The momentum of an object is defined by its mass and velocity. In sporting situations, the mass of an object (eg the performer's body, the piece of equipment) tends to stay the same for the duration of the event, so the momentum only changes when its velocity changes – the greater the velocity, the greater its momentum; the smaller the velocity, the smaller its momentum. Whenever the object is at rest, it has no momentum.

This chapter will look at how changes in momentum are achieved. The next section looks at this and introduces a new concept, **impulse.**

4.2 Increasing Momentum

If you have watched bob-sleigh racing, you will appreciate the importance of the start. The team work hard to give the sleigh as much momentum as possible before they jump on.

ACTIVITY 30

1 What would happen if you controlled the time allowed to push the sleigh? Explain the effect you would expect if you allowed the crew:

- one second:

- two seconds:

- three seconds:

2 What difference would it make if you reduced the number of people in the team? Explain the effect you would expect if you allowed:

- one pusher:

- two pushers:

- four pushers:

Now turn over.

You will probably have recognised that the longer the crew is allowed to push, the faster they will be going when they jump in the sleigh[1]. You may also have noticed that the crew will run further if it is allowed more pushing time.

Obviously the crew with four pushers would be able to generate much more force (over the same amount of time) than the single pusher. The four person crew would clearly get their sleigh travelling much faster than one person pushing.

There are two important messages here:

- The longer force is applied, the greater the change in momentum.
- The greater the force applied, the greater the change in momentum.

You can see that there are two factors which affect change in momentum:

- The time for which the force acts.
- The size of the force applied.

The combined effect of these two factors is called impulse. Read Panel K, and then try Activity 31.

Panel K: Impulse

When a force is applied to an object, the product of the force (F) and the length of time (t) that the force is applied, is called the **impulse** of the force.

This can be written as:

$$\text{Impulse} = Ft$$

Impulse is equal to Force x time, measured in newton seconds (Ns).

Remember:

$$\text{Momentum} = mv$$

Since a change in momentum is produced by the application of an impulse:

$$\text{Impulse} = \text{change in momentum}$$

or

$$Ft = \Delta\, mv$$

Δ is the greek letter delta which means *change in*.

---

1 This is true up to a point. After a certain time, the team will not be able to get the sleigh moving any faster.

You have learned about starting things moving to produce a required effect (ie pushing the bob-sleigh). The equation in Panel K shows, in mechanical terms, the relationship between the cause (the impulse applied) and the effect (the momentum generated). If you take a closer look at some of the effects you would like to produce, you can then come back to this equation and work out what has to be done to produce this effect.

ACTIVITY 31

1   Below is a list of activities that involve starting an object or a person moving. In each case, the object or person is initially stationary. Complete the questions over the page by selecting from the lists of activities and objects below. Leave the last three columns blank for the moment.

Activity	Object
• Tennis serve	• Tennis ball
• Sprint start	• Wheelchair racer
• Javelin throw	• Javelin
• Long jump	• Long jumper
• Throw in sumo wrestling	• Sumo wrestler
• Slap shot in ice hockey	• Puck
• Jump to catch high cross	• Football goalkeeper
• Rugby scrummage	• Opposition pack
• Golf drive	• Golf ball
• Weightlifting	• Weighted bar
• Tug of war	• Tug of war team

Continued...

- List the objects which have a smaller mass than the average person (ie less than nine stones or 60kg):

Object	Very Fast	Fast	Slow

- List the objects whose mass is about the same as an average person (ie between 9–14 stones or 60–90kg):

Object	Very Fast	Fast	Slow

- List objects whose mass is much greater than the average person (ie greater than 14 stones or 90kg):

Object	Very Fast	Fast	Slow

2 Now go back and tick the appropriate column to show approximately how fast each object is likely to be travelling:

- Very fast (faster than a man could run).
- Fast (running pace).
- Slow (walking pace or slower).

3 Now answer the following questions:

- How fast can you move objects with a small mass?

- How fast can you move objects with a large mass?

- Describe any other relationships:

Now turn over.

Generally you are able to move small masses very quickly, and you tend to move large masses very slowly. Those with a mass falling between the extremes tend to be moved at medium pace.

Normally, giving small masses high velocities helps to achieve the aim of projecting them as far or as high as possible (eg the golf ball). It can also increase the effectiveness of the activity, perhaps by making it more difficult for the opposition to deal with the object (eg bowling or batting in cricket). Performers frequently try to project themselves as far as possible (eg long jump, basketball rebound, volleyball block). However, they cannot project themselves as far or as fast as they can project smaller objects. Where activities require moving a large mass, it is not usually important to create a high velocity – success can be achieved simply by moving the object over a relatively small distance (eg weightlifting, rugby scrummaging or tug of war).

How relevant is this to your sport?

ACTIVITY 32

Select examples from your sport (if possible) where the performer needs to:

- move large masses with no need for high velocity (eg weightlifting, rugby scrummage):

- move small masses very quickly to achieve height or distance (eg javelin throw, cricket bowl, fast pass in netball or basketball):

- move medium masses as fast as possible (eg a volleyball player jumping to make a block at the net, a gymnast jumping for a somersault):

How is the performer able to generate this momentum? Look at Panel L.

Panel L: Generating Momentum

The sort of momentum changes seen in sport are directly related to muscle function[1]. Muscles are able to generate their greatest force when they act very slowly. Muscles can generate high velocities but only when they are working against a very light load.

The relationship shown in the graph below (Figure 37) is based on the results of experiments which investigated the amount of force a muscle could generate at various speeds of contraction.

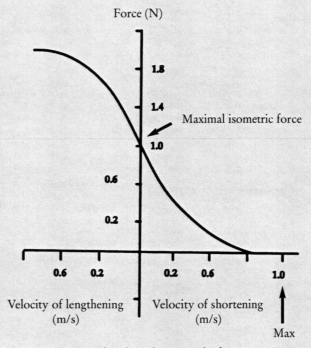

Figure 37: Force developed vs speed of contraction

The vertical (y) axis represents the amount of force generated by the muscle. The horizontal (x) axis represents the velocity of the contraction.

This shows that as the resistance increases, the rate at which the muscle shortens is reduced. This is because more of the muscle's capacity is required to generate the force and less is available for shortening it.

---

1   This is dealt with in more detail in the NCF home study pack entitled *An Introduction to the Structure of the Body*, available from Coachwise Ltd (0113 231 1310).

You can quite easily test out the ability of muscles to generate forces.

ACTIVITY 33

1 Tick the box beside the task you could perform most quickly:

☐ Lift your arm from your side, forwards and upwards to a horizontal position and back again, keeping it straight.

☐ Bend your finger through 90 degrees and back again.

2 Tick the box beside the body part that could lift the bigger mass:

☐ Right arm.

☐ Little finger.

You should have found that you were able to bend your finger faster but lift a heavier weight with your arm.

Sports have developed according to the physiological capabilities of the human body. The amount of impulse the body can generate depends on the size and strength of the muscles used to generate the force. If larger muscles are used, more force can be generated and therefore a greater change in momentum produced. Compare two athletes performing a 100m sprint, one running, the other in a wheelchair. The runner uses his leg muscles to generate momentum, whereas the wheelchair racer uses her arms. As the legs are bigger and stronger than the arms, the runner is able to generate momentum more rapidly than the wheelchair racer.

To summarise, you:

• often want to give small masses high velocities
• often want to move large masses slowly
• know that small muscles are able to generate lower forces and therefore less momentum
• know that large muscles are able to generate high forces and therefore a greater momentum.

In addition, you know that impulse = change in momentum:

• Ft = Δ mv (refer back to Panel K on Page 100).

How Can You Use This Knowledge to Optimise Technique?

To increase the change in momentum, you can either increase the size of the force applied or apply force for longer.

How can Small Masses be Projected at High Velocity?

You know that you cannot use the large muscles to apply extra force to a fast moving object, since these large muscles cannot contract quickly enough to keep up with the object.

However, you can increase the time for which force is applied to the object and this can be done in three ways:

- Using all the joints and muscles available.

- Using all the joints and muscles in sequence – largest to smallest.

- Using a large range of movement in each joint.

These principles have been applied in the development of many effective sports techniques. A good example is the technique used in the javelin throw (Panel M).

Panel M: The Javelin Throw

The fast moving joints in this action are in the throwing arm, which produces the rapid *hit* just before the javelin is released. However, the thrower also uses other joints (the ankles, knees, hips and vertebral column) in creating movement before this final stage. By using the legs and the trunk first, and also by rotating the arm through the greatest range of movement, the thrower is creating a *rolling start* from which to launch the javelin. Thus the javelin benefits not only from the velocity generated by the fast action of the thrower's shoulder muscle, but also from the additional velocity generated by the legs and trunk.

The principle described in Panel M is the principle behind the *step into* or *run up into* many throwing, batting, kicking and hitting activities.

 Is this used in your sport?

How To Move Heavy Objects

To change the momentum of heavy objects, a different strategy is required. As the mass of the object to be moved is large, a greater force is required. This force demands a greater amount of muscular work and so may involve more than one muscle group and joint action. In contrast to the case where a small load is accelerated to high speed by using muscles sequentially, heavy loads require the muscles to act together in a synchronised fashion. In this way, the effect of all the muscle actions is felt at the same time.

As the load increases, the action changes from more sequential to more synchronous along a continuum (see Figure 38):

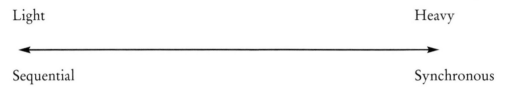

Light   Heavy

Sequential   Synchronous

Figure 38: The continuum of load and the coordination of muscle actions

4.3 Destroying Momentum

So far you have only learned about how to **increase** momentum, by increasing the force applied to an object or by applying force for longer. As mentioned earlier, landing, catching, intercepting and stopping are important applications of the principles of impulse and momentum. However, in these instances, you need to change the momentum a body already possesses.

 How can you slow objects down safely and effectively?

ACTIVITY 34

1 Imagine you are going to catch a cricket ball that has been lofted towards the boundary. Describe how you would cushion the ball as it is caught:

2 Now find a step, and jump from it, making your landing as soft as possible so that you do not feel any jarring. Describe how you soften the landing:

3 Describe what you would you do to intercept and trap a fast moving hockey ball (or football):

4 Describe the common features of these activities:

Now turn over.

In each of the situations in the last activity, the performer is trying to change momentum (bring the object to rest) by applying an impulse to the object.

You may have described an action that cushions the ball as it is caught which involves using the hands, arms, trunk and legs. By increasing the time component of the impulse applied to stopping the object, the force at any time during the stop is reduced. It may help to think of spreading the force out over a long period. At the other extreme, you could change the momentum of the object by applying a large force over a very short period. This is what tends to happen in a bad landing, catch or stop. In these cases performers fail to produce the appropriate movements and risk injury, as well as losing control of the object or themselves.

You may also have mentioned that during the catch and the landing, the limbs should initially be stretched out. In the landing, the ankles need to bend first, followed by the knees and finally the hips. In the catch, the fingers need to give first, followed by bending at the elbows and shoulders, and possible bending at the knees, hips and ankles.

If you think back to the sequencing of joint actions described earlier in the throwing actions, you will see that this sequence is reversed in stopping actions. In activities where the object was initially at rest, the large muscles were brought into action first, with smaller faster muscles being brought in as the action proceeded. In stopping activities, the object has its highest velocity just before the landing or catch begins. The first muscles brought into action are the small muscles which are able to match the speed of the incoming object most closely. They cannot generate a very high force, and only slow the object down a little. Gradually larger muscles are brought into play as the object slows down so that their action can be effective.

Finally, you may have suggested that the performer could reduce the impact force during the landing or the catch by using some sort of protective padding – perhaps a landing mat or glove respectively. These also work on the same principle. They slow the object down gradually, initially offering only a small resistance that increases as the padding is compressed.

In all the examples considered, the objects that were stopped had a small mass and high velocity (like the falling cricket ball), or a medium mass and a slow velocity (like jumping off the step). These rules apply in most situations but there are some exceptions – think about the ski jumper and the bob-sleigh team. Both these situations are slightly unusual – the ski jumper is a medium mass but travelling very quickly, the bob-sleigh team and their sleigh have a large mass and also travel at very high speeds.

? **How do these performers stop?**

You may well have pointed out that the ski jumper has a long distance (and time) over which to brake gradually. In some instances the terrain slopes upwards to help the skier gradually reduce velocity.

The bob-sleigh crew slow down by applying brakes (and because the snow at the base is often slushy it also increases friction). They also have a lengthy distance over which they can slow down. In this way they comply with the rules about slowing objects.

To summarise, objects can be slowed down safely and effectively by:

* increasing the time taken to slow the object down
* starting with the limbs extended and gradually giving as the catch, stop or landing proceeds
* using a soft compressible surface to cushion the blow.

Check your answers to Activity 34 against the rules above. If your answers are similar, then you are probably changing your momentum safely by spreading the force over a longer period.

4.4 Recap and Key Points

In this chapter you have looked at momentum and impulse and considered the implications to your own sport. It is now possible to produce a simple framework for analysing sports situations that involve starting and stopping.

If it involves **starting things moving**, think about:

- the size of the object to be moved
- the number of joints used
- when the joints are used
- how the joints are used.

Factors	To Start Large Objects Moving Slowly	To Start Small Objects Moving Quickly
Number of joints used	All joints	All joints
When the joints are used	All joints at once	In sequence (large to small)
How the joints are used	Use maximum range	Use maximum range

If it involves **stopping things moving**, think about:

- the size (and velocity) of the object to be stopped
- how the joints are used
- the stopping time
- other apparatus that increases stopping time.

Factors	To Slow Fast-moving Small Objects	To Slow Fast-moving Large Objects
How joints are used	Use in sequence (small to large)	Use in sequence (small to large)
Stopping time	Maximise to increase safety	Maximise to increase safety
Other apparatus	Padded gloves, nets	Large spaces, brakes, crash mats

To check your understanding of the concepts described in this chapter, try the following self tester.

SELF TESTER FOR CHAPTER FOUR

1   Name the two factors that determine how much momentum a body or object possess:

    •

    •

2   Name the two factors that affect the amount of impulse created during an impact:

    •

    •

3   List the three things a performer could do to project a small object as fast as possible (eg throw a cricket ball):

    •

    •

    •

Continued...

4 Think of a situation in your sport where the performer needs to project a small object as fast as possible (use another example from a different sport if your sport is inappropriate):

- Describe the situation:

- Describe the technique the performer uses in this situation:

- Using the three principles you listed in Question 3, describe how your performer could modify the technique to make the performance more effective:

5 List two things that a performer could do to move a large mass where velocity is unimportant:

-

-

6 Think of a situation in your sport where a performer needs to move a large mass, where velocity is unimportant:

• Describe the situation:

• Describe the technique the performer uses to move the mass:

• Using the two principles you listed in Question 5, describe how your performer could modify technique to become more effective:

Now turn over.

1 *Name the two factors that determine how much momentum a body or object possess:*
- *Velocity.*
- *Mass.*

2 *Name the two factors that affect the amount of impulse created during an impact:*
- *The size of force applied.*
- *The time for which force is applied.*

3 *List the three things a performer could do to project a small object as fast as possible (eg throw a cricket ball):*
- *Using all the joints and muscles available.*
- *Using all the joints in sequence – largest to smallest.*
- *Using a large range of movement in each joint.*

4 *Think of a situation in your sport where the performer needs to project a small object as fast as possible:*

The example of the javelin throw described in Panel M on Page 107 may help you to check your answer. If you need further help, seek the advice of an experienced coach in your sport.

5 *List two things that a performer could do to move a large mass where velocity is unimportant:*
- *Use all the joints and muscles available.*
- *Use all the available joints at the same time.*

6 *Think of a situation in your sport where a performer needs to move a large mass, where velocity is unimportant:*

Check with an experienced coach in your sport.

If you had any difficulty with this self tester, go back and reread the relevant parts before moving on to the next chapter.

4.5 Further Help

Bartlett, RM (1997) **Introduction to sports biomechanics.**
London, E & FN Spon. ISBN 0-4192-08402.
Chapter 2: Movement (kinematic) Considerations (pp47–69)
and Chapter 3: Linear and Angular Kinetics (pp82–99).

Dyson, GHG (1986) **Dyson's mechanics of athletics.**
8th edition. London, Hodder and Stoughton Educational. ISBN 0-340-39172-3.
Chapter 4: Forces (pp24–60).

Hall, S (1991) **Basic biomechanics**. St Louis MS, Mosby. ISBN 0-8016-2087-2.
Chapter 9: Movement Linear Kinematics (pp252–287)
and Chapter 11: The use of force (pp316–349).

Hay, JG (1993) **The biomechanics of sports techniques.**
4th edition. London, Prentice Hall. ISBN 0-13-084534-5.
Chapter 3: Linear Kinematics (pp13–46) and
Chapter 5: Linear Kinetics (pp60–110).

Going Round in Circles (Angular Motion)

5.0 Introduction

So far, you have considered only linear motion (ie motion in a straight line). This is the simplest form of motion and offers an ideal situation in which to introduce many simple mechanical principles. However, pure linear motion rarely occurs in sport – a bob-sleigh sliding down a flat, straight section of a run might be one possibility but does this ever occur? Most movements in sport involve some form of rotation.

What is Rotation?

In everyday terms, rotation can be described as circular motion, angular motion, motion in a circle, or in parts of a circle called arcs. A more precise scientific definition is given in Panel N.

Panel N: Angular Motion

Angular motion is the motion occurring when one point of an object is fixed (the axis of rotation) and all other points on the object rotate about the axis. In other words, angular motion is the motion occurring when points on an object do not move through the same distance in the same time.

It should be pointed out that just as it is rare to find examples of purely linear motion in sport, it is also unusual to find sporting examples of purely angular motion. One example is a skater spinning – but only as long as the spin is kept on the spot.

Most movements are a combination of rotation and linear motion. Linear motion includes movements in a straight line (rectilinear) or a curved line (curvilinear). The combination of rotation and either form of linear motion is referred to as **complex** or **general motion**. Study the examples over the page.

- The wheelchair racer in Figure 39 moves in a straight line down the track (rectilinear motion) by making the wheels of the chair turn about the axle (rotation).

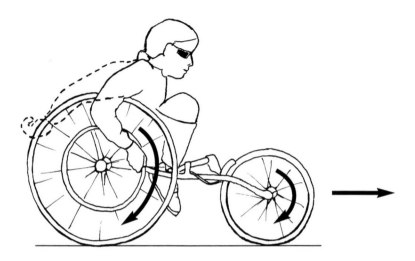

Figure 39: Complex motion in wheelchair racing

- Long jumpers follow a curvilinear pathway during the flight phase of the jump but their limbs rotate during the flight (Figure 40).

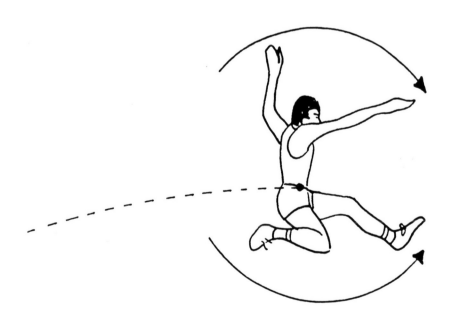

Figure 40: Complex motion in long jump

Rotation of the Limbs

Because of the structure of the body, the limbs work on the principle of rotation. For example, Figure 41 shows how the lower leg rotates at the knee joint when the quadriceps muscle contracts.[1]

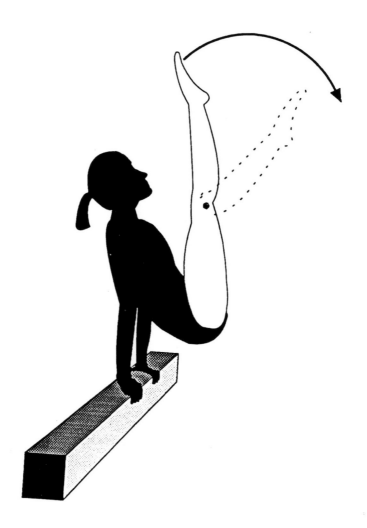

Figure 41: Joint rotation

Similarly, the arms rotate at the shoulder joint when throwing an object or swinging a bat, club or racket. In running, the foot rotates at the ankle joint, the lower leg rotates at the knee, while the whole leg rotates at the hip joint. In addition, the arms rotate backwards and forwards at the shoulder joint, and from side to side to balance the movement of the legs. Similar rotation occurs as the performer jumps and kicks. Even though the performer may run, jump, swim or paddle in a straight line, there must be rotation around the joints to produce this effect.

---

1   You are recommended to read the NCF home study pack *An Introduction to the Structure of the Body* for further details, available from Coachwise Ltd (0113 231 1310).

What Sort of Rotation is Needed?

In addition to rotation of the limbs, there are many instances in sport where the performer needs to rotate a whole object. This might involve:

- rotating the body (eg somersaulting in gymnastics, a triple axel in skating, or pivoting in netball or basketball)

- creating rotation in another person (eg throwing an opponent in judo, tackling in rugby)

- rotating an object (eg propelling a wheelchair, imparting spin to the ball in cricket or tennis).

Skilful tennis players know how to generate topspin and slice in order to make the ball shoot forward or stop short. The lofted face of a golf club gives the ball backspin, enabling players to gain maximum distance in a drive, or stopping the ball quickly when chipping onto the green. Swerve shots are also seen in sports where the ball is kicked (eg rugby and football), and where the ball is bowled or thrown (eg cricket and baseball).

Clearly rotation is involved in almost every aspect of sport. Performers must learn how to create the right amount of rotation, and control and use it efficiently and effectively. This chapter is designed to help you understand the general principles which allow the sports performer to do this.

By the end of this chapter you should be able to:

- explain what is meant by the terms **axis of rotation** and **plane of motion**

- list the three principal axes of rotation of the body and other common axes of rotation

- explain where the force must be applied in relation to the axis of rotation in order to produce or destroy rotation

- explain what is meant by **moment of inertia**

- describe how rotation is generated in a technique in your sport.

To analyse rotation, you first need to understand about axes and planes.

5.1 Axes of Rotation and Planes of Motion

The next activity will help you to recognise axes and planes.

ACTIVITY 35

For this activity, you will need a pencil and a small sheet of card.

1 Push your pencil through the card, making sure it is at right angles to the card as shown in Figure 42.

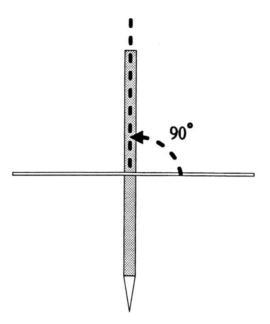

Figure 42: Model of an axis and a plane

You now have a model of an axis of rotation (your pencil) and a plane of motion (the card).

2 Mark a cross at the edge of the card. Make the card turn by twisting the pencil. Rotation occurs around the axis. Notice how the cross moves in a circle around the pencil. Movement occurs along a plane. The cross moves along the face of the card. Notice also how the axis and the plane (the pencil and the card) are perpendicular, that is at right angles (90 degrees) to each other.

If you are still not quite sure what is meant by the terms axis of rotation and plane of movement, read the definitions in Panel O.

Panel O: Axes and Planes

An **axis** of rotation is the imaginary line or point about which a body rotates. The **plane** of motion is the two-dimensional space cut by a moving body; the plane along which movement occurs.

Recognising Axes of Rotation

It is usually easier to recognise the axis of rotation when you stand and look along the axis of rotation, perpendicular to the plane of motion.

Place your pencil at the centre of the diagram of the wheel below (Figure 43), so that it points down into the page. Imagine a line passing through your pencil into the page. This line represents the axis of rotation of the wheel. The spinning of the wheel takes place along a plane represented by the page.

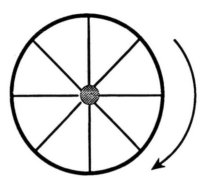

Figure 43: A spinning wheel

Now try Activity 35 again, but this time hold the pencil directly in front of your eye so that you can only see the end of the pencil. You are now looking along the axis of rotation, and the plane of motion (the card) is perpendicular to you. This may sound a bit complicated, but you almost certainly did this automatically when you first watched the cross on the card. The view you get should be similar to that shown in Figure 44.

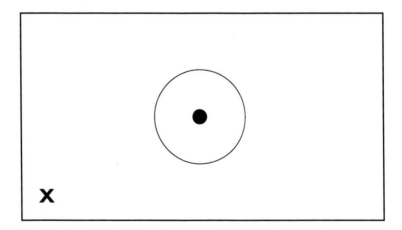

Figure 44: Looking along the axis of rotation

The round spot represents the end of the pencil, which coincides with the axis of rotation. Being able to create this view (either in a diagram, in your mind, or watching from a particular place), is a useful technique for analysing motion in sport. Try the next activity.

ACTIVITY 36

Mark the centre of rotation in each of the following diagrams with a cross. Then place the point of your pencil on the cross, holding the pencil vertically to locate the axis of rotation. In each of these examples, the axis of rotation passes through a joint in the body. Write down that particular joint for each of the following:

1

Figure 45: Footballer kicking ball

2

Figure 46: Gymnast stretching ankles

3

Figure 47: Games player doing warm-up side stretch

Now turn over.

Check your answers with the following:

1   *Hip joint.*

2   *Ankle joint.*

3   *Spinal column.*

In Question 3, there are actually several axes of rotation within the lumbar region during this activity.

Axes of Rotation of Limbs

Axes can be named according to their orientation, that is the direction in which they pass through the body. Axes passing from one side of the body to the other, from the left to the right (or vice versa), are called **transverse axes** (see Figure 48):

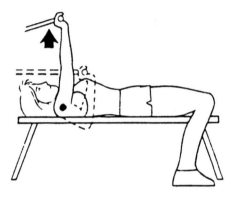

Figure 48: Transverse axes

Axes passing from the front to the back of the body (or vice versa), are called **anterior-posterior axes** (see Figure 49):

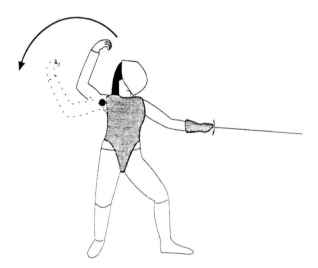

Figure 49: Anterior-posterior axes

Axes passing from the top to the bottom of the body (or vice versa), are called **longitudinal axes** (see Figure 50).

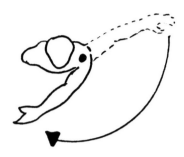

Figure 50: Longitudinal axes

ACTIVITY 37

Look back at the axes in Activity 36. Are they:

- transverse (T)
- anterior-posterior (A)
- longitudinal (L)?

Match the appropriate term. Describe the orientation of the axis of rotation in each of the following examples by placing a ring round the correct response:

- kicking ball: T   A   L
- stretching ankles: T   A   L
- sidestretch: T   A   L

Now turn over.

The correct answers are:

- *Kicking ball:*   *Transverse.*
- *Stretching ankles:*   *Transverse.*
- *Side stretch:*   *Anterior-posterior.*

So far you have looked at axes of the body. Now you need to identify the axes of rotation of objects spinning in flight (eg a ball, discus, performer).

Axes of Rotation of Objects in Flight

When performers are in the air, they will always rotate about an axis that passes through their centre of gravity[1]. Similarly a rotating object will always rotate about an axis that passes through its centre of gravity when it is in flight.

In Activity 36 on Page 125, the examples showed rotation occurring around axes that passed through joints. You classified these axes as anterior-posterior, longitudinal or transverse. The axes passing through the centre of gravity of the body can also be classified in the same way. The transverse, longitudinal and anterior-posterior axes passing through a performer's centre of gravity are also known as the body's three principal axes of rotation (Figure 51).

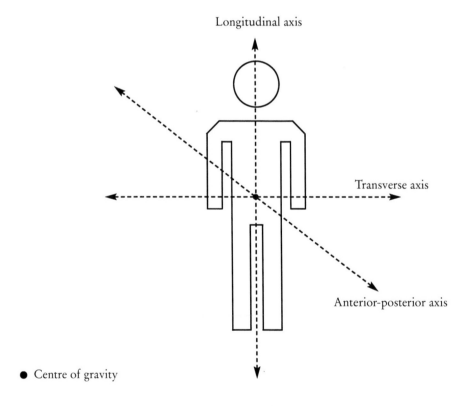

Figure 51: The principal axes of rotation

---

1   Refer back to Page 14 for a definition of centre of gravity if necessary.

Now try Activity 38.

ACTIVITY 38

Circle the correct axes involved in the following movements
(T = transverse, A = anterior-posterior and L = longitudinal):

1 Jump and simultaneously complete a half turn:

   T   A   L

2 Forward and backward somersaults by a gymnast, diver or trampolinist:

   T   A   L

3 Twisting movement by a gymnast, diver or trampolinist:

   T   A   L

4 Cartwheel by a gymnast:

   T   A   L

Now turn over.

Check your answers with the following:

1 *Longitudinal*
2 *Transverse*
3 *Longitudinal*
4 *Anterior-posterior.*

Reread this section if necessary.

Classifying human axes of rotation is fairly straightforward, since it is easy to distinguish front and back from left and right and so on. In some situations, this is not quite as clear. For example, the discus has one obvious axis of rotation about which it spins and which is usually called its longitudinal axis. However, because of its symmetrical shape, no one side of the discus can consistently be labelled right or left, back or front. Instead of having two distinct axes (anterior-posterior and transverse), the discus has an infinite number of axes passing across it. This means you could spin it like a coin on any part of its circumference. A sphere also has an infinite number of axes in all directions through its centre of gravity because of its regular shape.

External Axes, Complex Rotation and Axes that Move

In some situations the axis of rotation can be outside the body of the performer. For example, a gymnast swinging on a bar rotates about an axis passing along the length of the bar (Figure 52):

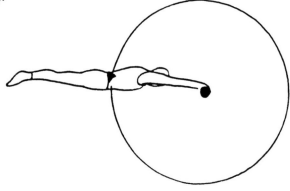

Figure 52: An external axis of rotation (bar)

If you catch your foot on something, you tend to rotate about an axis between your foot and whatever caught it (Figure 53).

Figure 53: An external axis of rotation (foot)

In many activities, the axis of rotation moves as the activity proceeds – a rolling ball rotates around an axis at the point of contact with the ground, the same is true of a performer who rolls on the ground (Figure 54).

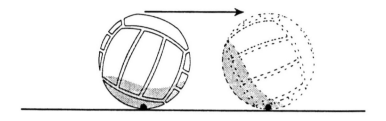

Figure 54: An axis that moves (ball)

In practice, rotation often happens around more than one axis at a time. Think of high jumpers who twist as they jump, or gymnasts or divers who twist as they somersault. Axes of rotation are not always horizontal or vertical – they may be diagonal, as in the wind up action of the hammer throw, or the golfer's swing (Figure 55).

Figure 55: Diagonal axis of rotation (golf)

You may be thinking that this is becoming rather complicated again. It is true that many sports activities involve complex rotations. However, if you focus on one part of the technique, you will be able to recognise the axes of rotation. You might like to practise this before moving on to the next section.

ACTIVITY 39

1 Watch performers in your own sport (this might be your own performers in action, or television/video recordings of performers).

- Pick one aspect of their technique to study.

- Move to, or imagine yourself to be in, the place that enables you to look along the axis of rotation.

- Draw a diagram to represent what is happening:

2 You should now be able to check your own work. If you correctly identified the axis of rotation, you should be able to:

- draw a dot on your diagram to show the position of the axis of rotation

- place your pen point on the dot and imagine that a line passing through your pen into the paper forms the axis of rotation

- draw the action as if it were taking place in the plane of the paper.

If you had any difficulty with this activity, reread the section.

5.2 **Generating Rotation**

Try Activity 40 which begins to explain how rotation is generated.

Many sports involve complex rotation.

ACTIVITY 40

1 Throw a tennis ball (or an apple or orange) into the air without spinning it. Draw a diagram to show the point of force application and the direction in which the force is acting:

2 Now throw the ball again but try to make it spin. Draw another diagram to show the point of force application and the direction in which the force was acting:

3 What did you do differently to make the ball spin? Describe what happened:

NB It may help you to mark the position of the ball's centre of gravity on the diagrams.

4   Balance a ruler on one finger of your left hand. Use your right hand to push on the ruler at the places shown in the diagram below. Push with the same force each time.

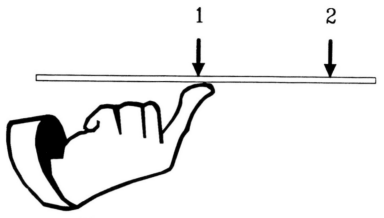

Figure 56: Ruler balanced on finger

Note what happened when you pushed:

* at position 1:

* at position 2:

Now turn over.

Activities 36 and 37 (Pages 125 and 127) should have shown you that for rotation to occur, a force must be applied eccentrically (ie not through the axis of rotation). In Activity 40 your first diagram should have looked like Figure 57, with the force applied upwards through the centre of gravity of the ball. Because the force acts through the centre of gravity of the ball, no rotation is produced.

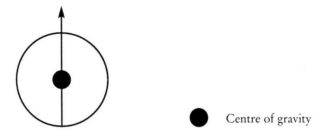

Figure 57: Throwing the ball with no rotation

To make the ball spin, you probably pulled or twisted your hand sideways. Your second diagram in Activity 40 should have looked like Figure 58.

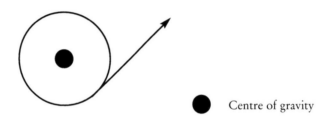

Figure 58: Making the ball spin

Notice that the force does not pass through the centre of gravity of the ball. Remember that airborne objects rotate about an axis through their centres of gravity, which is why it is necessary to know where the force acts in relation to this point.

In Question 4 the axis of rotation is located where the ruler rests on your finger. You should have found that you created a lot of rotation by pushing at the end of the ruler furthest from the axis of rotation. You should also have found that no rotation was produced when you pushed directly down through this axis of rotation.

This can be related once again to sport. If the footballer kicks a ball so the force is directed through the centre of gravity, the ball will travel forward without side spin (Figure 59a). It is very difficult to be as accurate as this – normally the ball travels with some side spin because the force is directed slightly to one side of the centre of gravity. Players learn to alter the amount of spin applied to achieve different effects – the further the force is directed from the centre of gravity, the greater the amount of spin (Figures 59b and c).

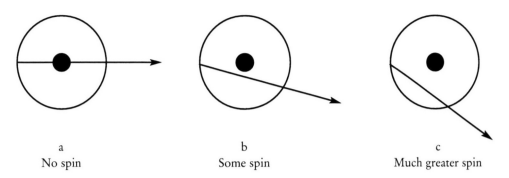

Figure 59: Controlling the amount of spin created

The technical name for a force creating rotation is torque (see Panel P).

Panel P: Torque

Torque is the name given to the turning effect produced by a force acting at some distance from an axis of rotation. The relationship between torque, the force (F) and the distance (d) from the axis of rotation at which the force acts is presented in the simple equation:

$$\text{Torque} = Fd$$

Therefore, torque is equal to the force multiplied by the distance from the axis of rotation in newton metres (Nm). The distance described here is the shortest distance between the line of action of the force and the axis of rotation, sometimes called the perpendicular distance between the line of action of the force and the axis of rotation. Remember that the line of action of a force is a straight line passing through the point of application of the force and extending indefinitely in the direction in which the force acts.

The amount of torque generated depends on how much force is applied and where the force is applied in relation to the axis. Recognising the perpendicular distance between the line of action of the force and the axis of rotation is not difficult as long as you remember that perpendicular means at right angles and the perpendicular distance is the shortest distance between two points (compare the length of the solid lines in Figure 60):

Figure 60: Perpendicular distance

The amount of torque generated depends on how much and from where force is applied.

ACTIVITY 41

Start with a familiar example – someone trying to push a door shut. To analyse the effectiveness of the push, you need to identify the perpendicular distance between the line of action of the force and the axis of rotation.

Remember the first step is to get the best view of the rotation. Figure 61a shows the view from above the door. Notice the door handle and the dot representing the location of the axis of rotation that runs down through the hinges:

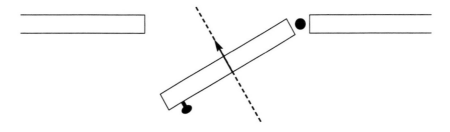

Figure 61a: Pushing the door shut

The solid arrow is the vector representing the force (see Chapter Two). You can see that the door has been pushed half-way between the handle and the hinges. The dotted line represents the line of action of the force. Remember that this also runs along the force arrow even though you cannot see it so clearly.

1   Draw a solid line from the dot to the dotted line so that it meets the dotted line making a right angle.

2   Now do exactly the same in the following diagram which shows the situation when someone has tried to close the door by pushing it close to the handle.

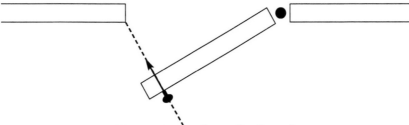

Figure 62a: Pushing the door shut

Now turn over.

You should find that the perpendicular distance between the line of action of the force and the axis of rotation is much smaller when the door is pushed half-way between the handle and its hinges. If the force applied in both situations is the same but the distance (d) is different, which situation will produce the greater torque? You should recognise that more torque is produced by pushing at the handle (Figure 62a) than by pushing between the handle and the hinges (Figure 61a). This reinforces what you intuitively know – the same amount of push will have a much greater effect when applied at the handle than when applied nearer the hinges.

Check your diagrams with the following:

1

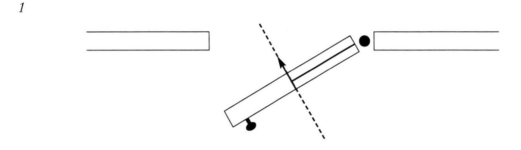

Figure 61b: Pushing the door shut

2

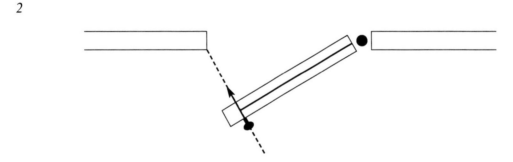

Figure 62b: Pushing the door shut

Remember that you are learning to recognise the perpendicular distance between the force and the axis of rotation because this is one factor that affects how much torque is generated. As mentioned earlier, the size of the force applied is the other key factor.

Knowing and being able to identify the factors that affect torque, should help you to compare different techniques in your sport and assess their effectiveness. Try the next activity.

ACTIVITY 42

1 Identify one technique in your sport where the performer needs to generate rotation:

2 Watch a good performance of this technique and identify the axis of rotation (you may need to refer back to Activity 35 on Page 123). Try to estimate the direction in which the force creating the rotation is acting. Then try to identify the perpendicular distance between the line of action of this force and the axis of rotation. Draw a diagram to record your observations:

3 Now watch a poor performance of the same technique. While you are still learning to analyse techniques in this way, it may be helpful to analyse a very bad performance so that the differences are clear to see. Repeat the steps described above, and draw another diagram:

4 Now compare your diagrams and note your findings. Remember that torque = force x distance:

Now turn over.

In the good technique, you might expect to find a:

- *stronger force*
- *larger perpendicular distance between the line of action of the force and the axis of rotation.*

In the poor technique, you might expect to find a:

- *weaker force*
- *smaller perpendicular distance between the line of action of the force and the axis of rotation.*

Check your observations and the analysis with an experienced coach in your sport or with a sport scientist.

Stopping Rotation

So far you have found that torque is needed to start rotation. Torque is also needed to stop a rotation. You talked about the torque that would be required to push a door shut. The door could be prevented from slamming shut by a person pushing against it on the other side.

Figure 63: Using torque to destroy rotation

Notice how the torque stopping the rotation is acting in the opposite direction to the original torque that started the rotation.

In this chapter, you have been asked to identify and analyse rotations in various situations. You will have found some objects easier to rotate than others.

Which objects were easy to rotate?

Which objects were hard to rotate?

The next section explains why some objects are harder to rotate than others.

5.3 Resistance to Rotation: Moment of Inertia

Start by attempting the next activity.

ACTIVITY 43

You will need a racket, club or bat of some description:

1 Hold the racket near one end and make a chopping action with your wrist. Estimate the amount of effort needed using the following scale:

Very little effort   Great effort

          1   2   3   4   5

2 Now hold the racket half-way along its length and try the same chopping action again. Now rate the amount of effort needed on the same scale:

Very little effort   Great effort

          1   2   3   4   5

3 Explain whether it was it easier to make the chopping action when you held the racket near the end or in the middle:

If you found no difference, try the activity again.

4 Try to explain why it was easier:

Now turn over.

You will have found that it is easier to chop when you hold the racket nearer the middle. This is because the mass of the implement is closer to the axis of rotation through the wrist.

In other words, an object's resistance to angular motion depends on how its mass is distributed around the axis of rotation. The technical term for resistance to angular motion is moment of inertia (see Panel Q).

Panel Q: Moment of Inertia

The reluctance or resistance of an object to start rotating (or change its rate of rotation) about a particular axis is referred to as its **moment of inertia.** This depends not only on the mass of the object but also on the distribution of the mass in relation to the axis of rotation. In other words, the closer the mass to the axis of rotation, the smaller the moment of inertia and the easier the object is to rotate; the greater the distance between the mass and the axis of rotation, the greater the moment of inertia and the more difficult the object is to rotate.

The precise relationship between the moment of inertia of an object (I), the mass of the object (m) and the average distance (r) between the mass and the axis of rotation is shown in the following equation:

$$I = mr^2$$

This shows that if the distance between the mass and the axis is doubled, the moment of inertia will be quadrupled.

There are many examples in sport where the performer is able to alter the distribution of mass in relation to the axis of rotation, in order to change the moment of inertia. For example, children play a modified version of tennis, called short tennis, which uses a shorter and lighter racket than the adult version. The moment of inertia of the racket has been reduced by:

- reducing the mass of the racket
- keeping the mass close to the axis of rotation.

This makes the racket easier to rotate, so it is much easier to swing and therefore more appropriate to the child's strength. If children do not have shortened rackets, you will often find that they will naturally reduce the moment of inertia by gripping the racket further up the handle.

In gymnastics, young children usually learn a tucked somersault before progressing to piked and straight somersaults. When gymnasts perform tucked somersaults, their mass is close to their axis of rotation through the centre of gravity. In contrast during a straight somersault, the body and legs are stretched away from the centre of gravity. This shape has a much greater moment of inertia and is consequently more difficult to perform.

Think about the movement of the leg in walking. The axis of rotation about which the whole leg swings is a transverse axis through the hips. The leg remains fairly straight throughout the action – during both the support phase (when the weight is supported) and the recovery phase (when the leg swings forward for the next step). The moment of inertia of the leg about the hip joint remains fairly constant and near its maximum value throughout the stride (Figure 64).

Figure 64: A high moment of inertia during walking

In contrast, the leg becomes very bent during the recovery phase of a sprint stride (Figure 65).

Figure 65: A small moment of inertia during sprinting

By bending the leg at the knee, the mass of the leg is brought close to the axis of rotation through the hip – the moment of inertia of the leg about the hip has been reduced. This makes it easier to rotate and so it can be swung forward more quickly into the correct place for the next stride.

Check your understanding of this idea by working through the next activity.

ACTIVITY 44

1 Think about the recovery phase of a front crawl stroke (ie the part of the stroke when the arm is out of the water). Describe what the swimmer might do to swing the arm forwards into the water as quickly as possible:

2 Describe how the tennis player might reduce the effort involved in taking the racket back in preparation for a forehand drive:

You should have recognised that the swimmer could bend the arm at the elbow, bringing the mass of the arm closer to the axis of rotation through the shoulder. This reduces the moment of inertia of the arm about the shoulder and should make it easier to swing the arm forwards. In a similar way the tennis player might bend the elbow as the racket is swung back, also reducing the moment of inertia of the racket and arm about the shoulder. The tennis player also has the option of selecting a different racket – one with a smaller mass, to reduce the moment of inertia and make the movement easier.

5.4 Recap and Key Points

In this chapter the concepts of axes of rotation, planes of movement, torque and moment of inertia have been introduced. The next section combines these ideas to produce a simple analysis framework to help you apply this information to your own sport.

If it involves rotation, identify the:

- axis of rotation
- point of application of force
- direction in which the force acts.

Think about the:

- amount of force required
- perpendicular distance from line of action of the force to axis of rotation
- moment of inertia of the rotating object.

Factors	To Decrease Rotation	To Increase Rotation
Amount of force	Reduce the force acting in the same direction as rotation	Increase force acting in the same direction as rotation
Perpendicular distance from line of action of the force to axis of rotation	Reduce the distance	Increase the distance
Moment of inertia	Increase	Decrease

To check your understanding of the concepts described in this chapter, try the self tester over the page.

SELF TESTER FOR CHAPTER FIVE

1 Describe what is meant by the term **axis of rotation:**

2 Explain what is meant by the term **plane of motion:**

3 Label the diagram below which shows the three principal axes of the body:

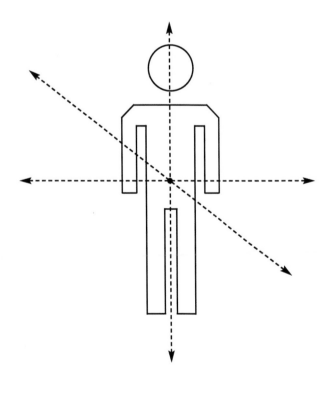

4   The following examples involve rotation about a transverse (T), anterior posterior (A) or longitudinal (L) axis. Circle the appropriate letter.

- Leg kick in front crawl: T   A   L
- Backward roll: T   A   L
- Skater spinning on ice: T   A   L
- Cartwheel: T   A   L
- Tennis player playing a forehand drive: T   A   L

5   Explain what is meant by the term **torque**:

6   Identify the two factors that affect the amount of torque generated:

-

-

7   Explain what is meant by the term **moment of inertia**:

8   A tennis player is swinging the arm back in preparation for a forehand drive. How could the technique be modified to make this action easier?

Now turn over.

1 **Describe what is meant by the term axis of rotation:**

The imaginary line or point about which a body rotates.

2 **Explain what is meant by the term plane of motion:**

The two dimensional space cut by a moving body. Activity 35 will help you to check your understanding of this idea.

3 **Label the diagram below which shows the three principal axes of the body:**

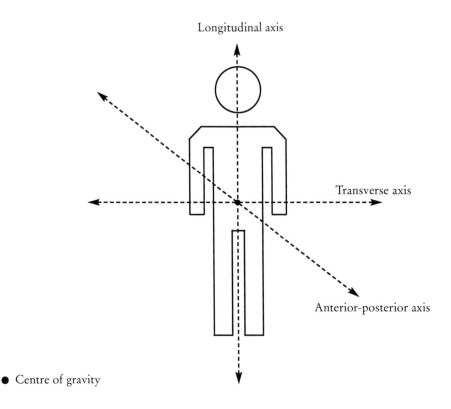

4 **The following examples involve rotation about a transverse (T), anterior posterior (A) or longitudinal (L) axis. Circle the appropriate letter.**

- *Leg kick in front crawl:*   T
- *Backward roll:*   T
- *Skater spinning on ice:*   L
- *Cartwheel:*   A
- *Tennis player playing a forehand drive:*   L

5 **Explain what is meant by the term torque:**

Torque is the name of the turning force that creates rotation.

6 *Identify two factors that affect the amount of torque generated:*
- *The size of the force applied.*
- *The perpendicular distance between the line of action of the force and the axis of rotation.*

7 *Explain what is meant by the term moment of inertia:*

Moment of inertia is the reluctance or resistance of an object to start rotating, or change its rotation about an axis. Moment of inertia depends on the mass of an object, and the distribution of the mass about the axis of rotation.

8 *A tennis player is swinging the arm back in preparation for a forehand drive. How could the technique be modified to make this action easier?*

By bending the arm in preparation for the drive. This would bring the mass of the arm closer to the longitudinal axis of rotation through the shoulder and reduce the moment of inertia of the arm about this axis.

If you had any difficulty with this self tester, go back and reread the relevant parts before moving on to the next chapter.

5.5 Further Help

Bartlett, RM (1997) **Introduction to sports biomechanics.**
London, E & FN Spon. ISBN 0-4192-08402.
Chapter 2: Movement (kinematic) Considerations (pp73–77)
and Chapter 3: Linear and Angular Kinetics (pp105–123).

Dyson, GHG (1986) **Dyson's mechanics of athletics.**
8th edition. London, Hodder and Stoughton Educational. ISBN 0-340-39172-3.
Chapter 5: Angular Motion (pp65–122).

Hall, S (1991) **Basic biomechanics.** St Louis MS, Mosby. ISBN 0-8016-2087-2.
Chapter 10: Movement Angular Kinematics (pp288–315)
and Chapter 13: Movement Angular Kinetics (pp388–415).

Hay, JG (1993) **The biomechanics of sports techniques.**
4th edition. London, Prentice Hall. ISBN 0-13-084534-5.
Chapter 4: Angular Kinematics (pp47–59) and
Chapter 6: Angular Kinetics (pp111–177).

Everything's Up in the Air (Projectile Motion)

6.0 Introduction

In previous chapters, you have looked at the forces performers have to generate in order to launch themselves or other objects into the air. You have considered how rotation of the limbs is necessary to achieve this and how the limbs can also be used to give objects rotation.

In this chapter, you will be looking at how objects are projected into the air and what happens to them when they are in the air (whether or not they have spin). Try the next activity.

ACTIVITY 45

Think of your own sport and jot down any situations where the performer or an object are in flight:

-

-

-

-

-

Now turn over.

Depending on your sport, you were probably able to write down a number of situations. Many sports involve projecting an object (eg a ball, a javelin, an arrow) and in most sports, the performers propel themselves or someone else. Remember that there is a brief moment when the performer is airborne in the running action. Reflect also on how many sports involve jumping.

The study of the movement of objects in flight is called **projectile motion** and as you will already have realised, an understanding of the factors that influence the trajectories of objects is important in sport.

Many of the principles described here are also relevant to performers who move through water. The types of forces created (drag force and lift force) are the same as those created when a body or object moves through the air.

In this chapter you will examine how objects are projected into the air and study the factors that affect the trajectory of objects once they are airborne. By the end of this chapter you should be able to:

- explain how the release point of an object affects its trajectory
- describe how to adjust the amount of lift or drag force affecting an object
- describe the effects that may result from putting spin on a ball in flight
- analyse techniques in your sport where the release point, drag or lift forces may affect the object or performer, and so modify these techniques to achieve the most effective performance.

6.1 Tangent Release Principle and Parabolas

Almost every activity results from rotation of the limbs (refer back to Chapter Five). Rotation is also important in activities in which objects are thrown, hit or kicked into the air. For example the:

- arm swings through an arc to throw or strike an object
- leg swings through an arc to kick an object.

You will already be familiar with some of the factors that affect the flight path of an object, for example the:

- amount of force that is applied
- point of application of the force
- direction in which the force is applied.

The next section explains two new rules that will enable you to predict the:

- direction in which an object will travel when it is first released
- pathway it will follow in flight.

Start by working through the next activity.

The flight path is affected by the amount of force applied, its point of application and direction.

ACTIVITY 46

You will need a partner, a tennis ball and a large space in which to carry out this activity.

You will need to give your partner the following instructions:

- You will be asked to throw the ball underarm four times.

- Please stand still during the throw.

- Keep your arm straight with a firm wrist.

- Before each throw, I will tell you when to release the ball (eg as your wrist passes your hip in the first example).

Check that this is understood.

Your task is to observe and then record the flight path of the tennis ball. Watch from the side and then, on the following diagrams, draw in the flight path of the tennis ball.

1   Release the ball as your wrist passes your hip (show where you mean):

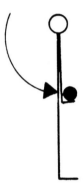

Figure 66a: Throw 1

2   Release the ball when your arm is at a low diagonal (show where you mean):

Figure 67a: Throw 2

3   Release the ball as your arm reaches the horizontal (show where you mean):

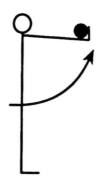

Figure 68a: Throw 3

4   Release the ball when your arm is at a high diagonal (show where you mean):

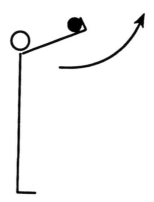

Figure 69a: Throw 4

Now turn over.

Your diagrams should look like these:

1 *Trajectory of ball released as wrist passes hip:*

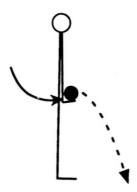

Figure 66b: Throw 1

2 *Trajectory of ball released when arm is at a low diagonal:*

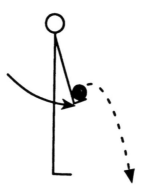

Figure 67b: Throw 2

3 *Trajectory of ball released when arm reaches the horizontal:*

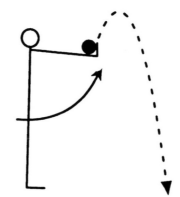

Figure 68b: Throw 3

4   *Trajectory of ball when arm is at a high diagonal:*

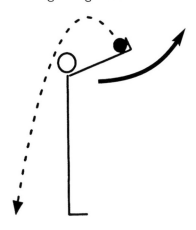

Figure 69b: Throw 4

If your diagrams were very different from Figures 66b–69b, go back and repeat Activity 46. Make sure that your partner is releasing the ball at the right place without bending the elbow or flicking the wrist.

As you watch your partner you may have noticed that the arm swings through an arc before releasing the ball (if you did not notice this, go back and watch several throws again). Initially, an object will fly at a tangent to the arc it was following at the moment of release. This is explained in more detail in Panel R over the page.

Panel R: Tangents

A tangent is a straight line that meets a curved line without crossing it. At the point where they meet, the tangent and the curved line have the same direction:

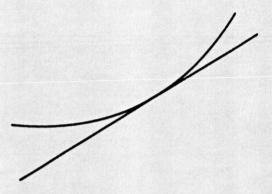

Figure 70: Tangent

When the straight line is a tangent to a circle, a radius (r) of the circle will meet the tangent at right angles:

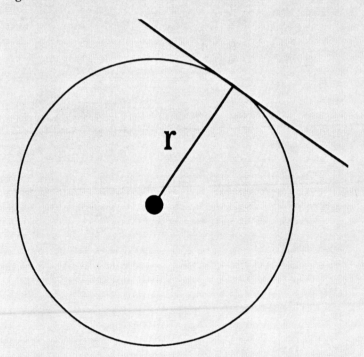

Figure 71: Tangent to a circle

This information provides a more systematic way of working out the direction in which an object will travel after release.

ACTIVITY 47

Look at Figure 72a which shows the second throw from Activity 46.

- Imagine that the arm swing is part of a circle.

- Mark a dot on the circle to represent the point at which the object will be released.

- Draw a line from the centre of the circle to the dot. This line is the radius of the circle. Notice that the centre of the circle corresponds with the performer's shoulder and the radius of the circle overlays the performer's arm.

- Find the tangent by drawing a line that just meets the circle at the dot and is perpendicular to the radius of the circle.

- The tangent indicates the direction in which the ball will initially travel after release.

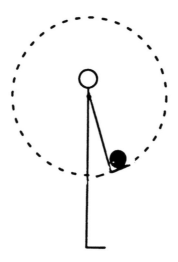

Figure 72a: Predicting the initial pathway of a projectile

Now turn over.

Check your diagram with the one below:

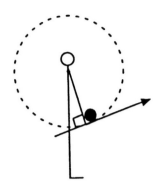

Figure 72b: Predicting the initial pathway of a projectile

This technique can be used in many sporting situations to predict the initial direction in which an object will travel. The second rule you must consider concerns the shape of the pathway of an object or performer in flight. In Activity 46 your partner threw the tennis ball four times. Each time the path of the tennis ball was a special shape called a **parabola.** Read Panel S for more information about parabolas.

Panel S: The Parabola

A parabola is a symmetrical shape. On level ground, a ball thrown at an angle of 45 degrees above the horizontal would also land at an angle of 45 degrees to the horizontal. It would be travelling with the same speed at take-off and landing, and it would reach its highest point midway between take-off and landing.

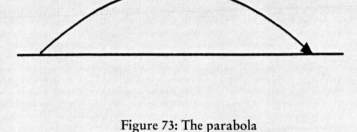

Figure 73: The parabola

The tennis ball thrown in Activity 46 (if it was only thrown a short distance) probably followed a pathway close to a parabola. However, not all objects follow parabolic pathways. Activity 48 should help you understand this.

ACTIVITY 48

1 Ask a partner to throw a table tennis ball as far as possible (try to do this in a place where there are no draughts or wind). Watch the throw from the side and try to draw the shape of the pathway followed by the ball. Record your drawing and any comments below:

2 Now ask your partner to throw a golf ball so it travels approximately the same distance as the table tennis ball. Draw the pathway:

3 Explain how the two flight paths differ:

Now turn over.

You will have found that the flight path of the table tennis ball was asymmetrical. It probably dropped to the ground at a much steeper angle than it was thrown. The ball therefore would have reached its highest point more than half-way towards the landing point. The golf ball would have followed the symmetrical parabola more closely.

This activity should have helped you to realise that although in theory all objects will follow parabolic flight paths, in reality this is not the case. Technically an object will only follow an exact parabola when projected in a vacuum near the Earth's surface – a situation that does not occur in everyday sport. In reality the object has to push its way through the air and this affects its flight path. Figure 74 below shows the theoretical and actual flight paths of a cricket ball.

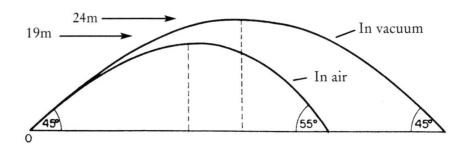

Figure 74: Theoretical and actual trajectories of a cricket ball

So far you you have only considered objects thrown through the air. Air resistance is obviously an important factor in sports performance – one that sportspeople need to understand. Similarly, water has a dramatic effect on objects and performers moving through it.

Air and water affect objects and performers in similar ways and both are classed as fluids. The study of how objects move through air or water or other liquids is called fluid mechanics. In the next section you will look more closely at some aspects of fluid mechanics, in particular two different forms of drag and the factors that affect it.

6.2 Drag Force

Drag force is the technical term for the resistance that an object encounters when it moves through air and water. Like friction (see Chapter Two), drag force always opposes a body's motion and tends to slow it down. The resistance you feel when you run into a head wind or try to walk through water, is due to drag force.

Before looking at specific examples in sport, you need to grasp the basic principles. When you first read the next section, it might seem a little difficult but bear with it, it should all make sense by the end of the chapter.

Physicists have investigated drag forces by placing objects in wind tunnels and blowing air past them, simulating the conditions that would exist in flight. By releasing smoke trails (or streamlines) and watching how these move around the object, it is possible to see the pathway the air takes around the object. From these observations, it is possible to detect variations in fluid flow and pressure around the object, and therefore predict what forces are acting on the projectile. In a slow airflow the streamlines around a ball look like the ones shown in Figure 75:

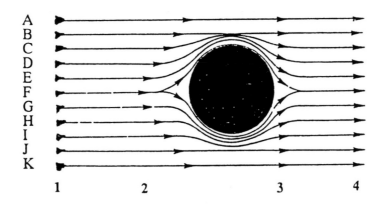

Figure 75: Streamlines in a slow fluid flow

NB In this and the following diagrams, you should assume that the air flow is moving from left to right across the page, and that the ball is travelling from right to left across the page.

Imagine that each of the lines A–K represents an individual smoke trail that marks the flow of the air in that region. Smoke trails A, B, J and K are unaffected by the presence of the ball and flow in a straight line past it. The smoke trails closer to the ball (C–I) are affected by the presence of the ball and have to divert their flow between points 2 and 3 to move past it. This results in the airstreams crowding together as they pass the widest part of the ball. As the airstreams have to move further to get round the ball, they must travel faster.

The situation is similar to the conditions found in a river. Where the river banks are wide apart, the river runs relatively slowly. This is similar to the relatively slow moving air in the wide airstreams before and after the ball. When the river is forced through a narrower channel (such as a gorge), it flows much faster. This is similar to the air that is forced to flow more quickly through the narrow channels each side of the ball. In situations where the flow is slow and streamlined, the most influential form of drag is surface drag or skin friction.

Surface Drag

When the air flow around an object is slow and streamlined, a very thin layer of air called the **boundary layer** sticks to the surface of the ball. This layer of air next to the ball tends to stick to the next layer of air pulling it along. In air, the sticking effect between the boundary layer and the ball and between subsequent layers of air is very weak. This is because air has low viscosity – there is very little friction between the air molecules and the layers slide past each other easily. In a more viscous fluid, such as water, the sticking effect between the ball and the boundary layer and between subsequent layers of fluid, is much greater. This greater friction makes it difficult to move through water and objects are slowed more in water than they are in air. Imagine how much more difficult it would be to move through a very viscous fluid such as treacle.

Surface drag increases when the object:

- has a rough surface
- travels rapidly through the fluid
- has a large surface area parallel to the flow.

The first point explains why swimmers shave to remove body hair, and why it is important for them to have close-fitting, smooth swimsuits – both reduce surface drag. In fact, most performers or objects travel too quickly to maintain a smooth, streamlined flow of fluid around them. Although surface drag continues to affect performance, it has a much smaller effect than profile drag which is considered in the next section.

Profile Drag

Start with Activity 49.

ACTIVITY 49

1 Move your hand slowly through a bowl full of water and notice the eddy currents which form behind it. Draw a diagram to show the movement of the water around and behind your hand:

2 Now try moving your hand quickly through the water and draw another diagram to show the movement of the water around and behind your hand:

3 Compare the two diagrams and explain how and why they are different:

Now turn over.

You will have found that as you moved your hand through the water a turbulent wake formed behind it. Your diagrams will probably have looked something like these:

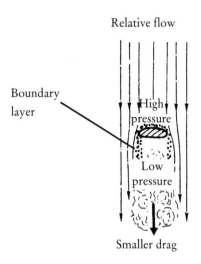

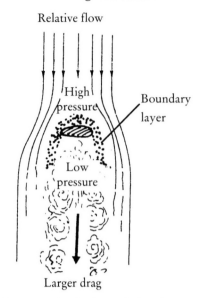

Figure 76[1]: Turbulence behind slow moving hand

Figure 77: Turbulence behind fast moving hand

The pressure on the leading surface of your hand is much greater than the pressure on the trailing surface of your hand. In a situation like this, the fluid is flowing too fast to stick to the surface of the object – in Activity 49 you will have noticed that the water did not stick to the surface of your hand. If you did not notice this, try the activity again. Look carefully behind your hand. You should see that the water is dragged away and forms a wake, leaving a space a behind your hand.

When this happens, the boundary layer is dragged away from the surface of the object. This boundary layer separation and the differences in pressure around the object create the turbulence you saw when you dragged your hand through the water. In the next section you will consider four factors affecting profile drag. This sort of drag is called profile drag because the profile, or area of the object facing the flow, is one factor that affects the amount of drag generated. Turbulence slows your hand down and is a form of drag.

Go back to Activity 49 and try moving your hand through the water palm first and then slicing it through the water with your thumb leading. Notice what happens and think about it as you read the next section.

Cross-sectional Area

If the area perpendicular to (ie facing) the flow is doubled, then the profile drag will also be doubled. There is a special rule determining the amount of profile drag experienced by a ball as it travels through the air. Try the next activity to find out about this rule.

1   Figures 76–81 and 84–86 have been adapted from Daish, CB (1972) **The physics of ball games.**

ACTIVITY 50

The resistance a ball meets in flight is dependent on its cross-sectional area. (If you cut an orange in half, the flat surface is the cross-sectional area.) The cross-sectional area of a ball is related to its diameter, so the resistance a ball meets in flight depends on its diameter. The profile drag a ball experiences is related to its diameter. You can work this out for yourself.

1   On the graph paper below, draw two circles – one 4cm (2") in diameter and the other 2cm (1") in diameter.

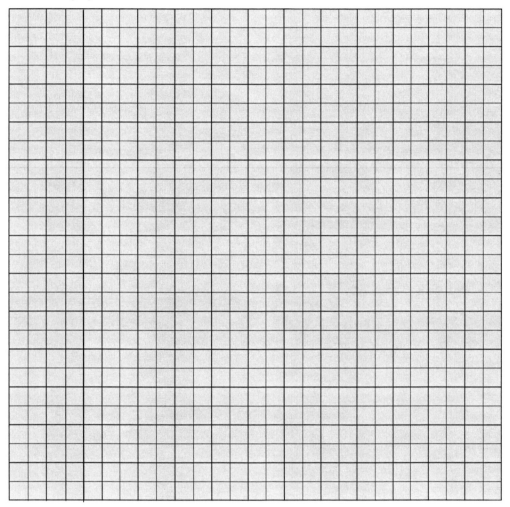

2   Now count the number of squares in each circle:
   • The 4cm circle contains _____ squares.
   • The 2cm circle contains _____ squares.

Now turn over.

You should have found that the larger circle contained four times as many squares as the smaller one. If the diameter of the ball is doubled, then its cross-surface area is quadrupled and the drag force is also quadrupled.

Velocity

Look back at the two diagrams you drew in Activity 49. You should have found that the faster you dragged your hand, the more turbulence you created. In fact, drag force is proportional to the square of the velocity with which the object travels through the fluid. This means that when velocity is doubled, the drag force exerted on the object is quadrupled.

This is the **relative velocity** – the velocity with which the fluid passes the object. This is true until the object reaches a critical velocity when the drag force is suddenly reduced. If you are interested in finding out more about this critical velocity, there are some references at the end of this chapter.

Another factor that influences the amount of profile drag experienced by an object is the shape of the object.

Streamlining

If the object (eg the ball) can be shaped to fill the space that would normally be filled with turbulence, drag can be reduced. Compare the turbulence created when a rugby ball is thrown along its longitudinal axis (a) and upright into a headwind (b):

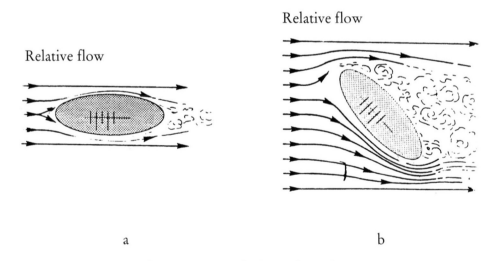

a   b

Figure 78: Streamlining reduces drag

Streamlining works by enabling the fluid to flow undisturbed along the surface of the object. Any irregularities or abrupt changes in the object's shape, disturb the flow of the liquid and result in turbulence. This turbulence then slows the object down.

This principle has led to the development of various aerodynamic designs in a number of sports – think of the tapered helmets that sprint cyclists wear, the sleek shape of modern racing cars and the low crouched position adopted by speed skiers.

Fluid Density

Water has a much higher density than air, so the drag forces produced when moving through water are much larger than those produced when moving through air. Air density can also vary as a result of different weather conditions, or as a result of different altitudes. If you are interested in finding out more about these effects, follow up the references at the end of the chapter.

There is one last factor to be considered in relation to the cross-sectional area, velocity and streamlining which affect the amount of drag an object experiences. Think back to Activity 48 in which you threw a golf ball and a table tennis ball. The golf ball and table tennis ball:

- have similar cross-sectional areas
- were thrown a similar distance and therefore with similar velocity
- are similarly shaped
- travelled through similar air conditions.

 Why was the table tennis ball affected so much more than the golf ball?

In fact, the drag force these balls experienced is very similar. Read on to find out what caused the difference in performance.

Mass

The reason the table tennis ball was so greatly affected is explained when you consider the mass of the two balls. The golf ball has a larger mass than the table tennis ball and a much greater inertia (resistance to changes in its motion). This means that the drag force experienced during flight only slows it slightly. In contrast, the table tennis ball has a smaller mass and a smaller resistance to changes in its motion. The same drag force produces a much greater deceleration and results in the asymmetrical flight path you observed.

So far in this section the concentration has been mainly on the drag forces that oppose an object's motion through a fluid. In many cases drag force is not the only force acting on an object. The object may also experience a lift force. In the remainder of this chapter, you will consider the factors that affect the amount and type of lift force a body experiences.

Lift force.

6.3 Lift Force

Try the next activity.

ACTIVITY 51

1 Hold a strip of paper close to your face just underneath your lips. Blow hard over the paper. What happens? Try blowing harder and then more gently and jot down what happens:

2 Now try holding the paper vertically and blow along one side of it. Jot down what happens:

Now turn over.

You will have found in the first exercise that the paper lifts as you blow over it. The harder you blow, the more the paper will lift. By blowing over the paper you are making the air above it move.

What is happening is explained by the work of a Swiss scientist named Daniel Bernoulli. He found a relationship between the rate of flow of a liquid and the pressure of a liquid. He showed that:

- where flow is slow, pressure is high
- where flow is fast, pressure is low.

According to Bernoulli's principle, fast flowing air has lower pressure than slow moving or stationary air. So the pressure of the moving air above the paper is less than the pressure below the paper. The resulting pressure force from below the paper pushes it upwards.

Similarly, in the second exercise, the air you blew along one side of the paper was moving more quickly than the air on the other side of the paper. This also created a pressure difference and pushed the paper sideways towards the side that you blew along.

This demonstrates the principle upon which aeroplane wing design is based. Because of the wing shape, air is forced to travel more rapidly over the top of the wing than below it. This produces a relatively low pressure zone above the wing and a relatively high pressure zone below the wing. The result is that the wing experiences an upward lift force.

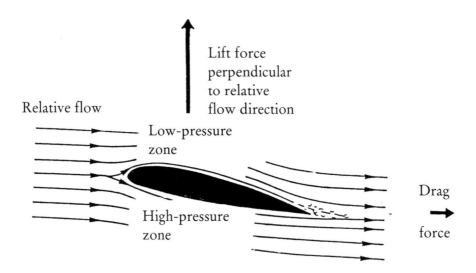

Figure 79: The aerodynamic properties of the wing shape

However, an object does not need to be wing-shaped to generate lift forces. For example, the discus is symmetrically shaped when viewed from the side. If the discus was thrown horizontally into an airflow (Figure 80), air would travel at an equal velocity along its upper and lower surfaces. There would be no pressure difference and so no lift force. If the discus was thrown tilted relative to the airflow (Figure 81), air would travel faster over the upper surface than under the lower surface.

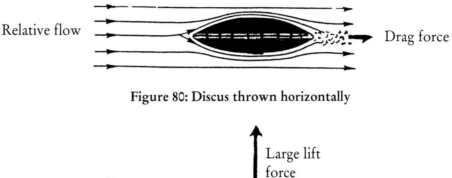

Figure 80: Discus thrown horizontally

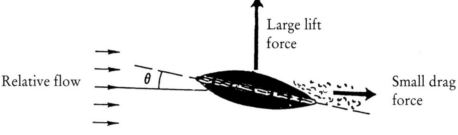

Figure 81: Discus tilted relative to the air flow

The result should be relatively high pressure under the discus and relatively low pressure over the discus. Consequently a lift force would act on the discus. Does this mean the discus should be released with as great an angle as possible?

The larger the tilt, the larger the lift – up to a critical point, at which large drag forces are encountered. Beyond this critical point (the **stall angle**), lift force diminishes and drag force increases dramatically. The skill of discus throwing is to maximise the lift force while minimising the drag force that acts on the discus. In the previous section the factors affecting drag force were considered. The next section briefly reviews four factors that affect lift force:

- The coefficient of lift
- Velocity
- Surface area
- Air density.

The Coefficient of Lift

The coefficient of lift is a number indicating how well a particular object can create lift force in airflow. This depends not only on the shape of the object but also its angle of attack (ie the angle at which it projects into the air or fluid) with respect to the airflow. Remember how the discus only generated lift when tilted with respect to the airflow.

Velocity

As with drag force, lift force increases as the object's velocity increases. If the velocity of the object doubles, the drag force quadruples.

Surface Area

Like drag force, lift force is affected by the surface area of the object. However, it is not the surface area facing the airflow that is the crucial factor. Instead it is the surface area inclined to form the angle of attack that affects how much lift is generated. This is why ski jumpers lean their bodies and skis at an angle to the air flowing past them.

Air Density

The more dense the fluid, the greater the lift force an object will experience.

In many of the examples cited, the lift force has in fact lifted the object (eg the discus, the aeroplane wing, the piece of paper in the first part of Activity 51). However, lift forces do not always act upwards as was demonstrated in the second part of Activity 51.

6.4 Swimming

Swimmers have to generate forces in the water to propel their body down the pool. You might think that they move by 'pulling on the water', but this is not really the case. Activity 52 should help you understand this.

ACTIVITY 52

1 Place your hand in a bowl of water and pull it straight backwards so that the palm of your hand leads the movement. Draw a diagram to show the force acting on your hand.

2 Now move your hand from side to side in the water and adjust the angle between your hand and the direction of movement. Note what happens and draw a diagram to show the force you think is acting on your hand.

Now turn over.

---

1   *You should have noticed that when you pulled your hand backwards through the water, a drag force was acting in the opposite direction to the movement of your hand.*

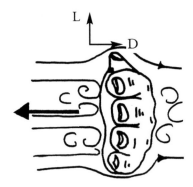

**Figure 82: Drag force acting in the opposite
direction to the movement of the hand**

2   *When you moved your hand from side to side, a lift force was generated due to the angle between your hand and the movement.*

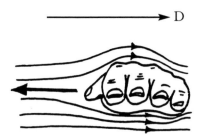

**Figure 83: Lift force being generated due to the
angle between the hand and movement**

Swimmers use both drag and lift forces to make their body move. During the stroke, they pull their hand backwards through the water and a drag force is produced. As their hand is moving backwards relative to their body, this drag force acts to propel them down the pool. Swimmers also move their hand from side to side to create a lift force. Skilled swimmers know how to adjust the angle of their hand to generate a lift force in the right direction to propel their body.

6.5 The Spinning Ball

So far, we have considered lift forces produced due to the shape or angle of a body relative to its motion. Many sports involve the use of spin to change the flight path of a projectile as it moves through the air.

? What causes the ball to dip or swerve in flight?

In this section, slice, topspin and sidespin will be explained.

Slice or Bottom Spin

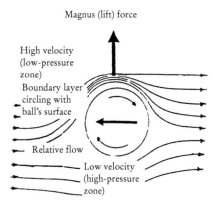

Figure 84: The effect of slice on the boundary layer (side view)

Figure 84 shows a ball hit with bottom spin. As the ball spins, some of the air in the boundary layer is dragged around the ball in the direction of the spin. This causes more air to flow round the top of the ball than under it. As shown earlier in Section 6.3, the air at the top must be moving faster than the air below. There is therefore a pressure difference with more pressure below the ball than above it. This pressure difference creates a net force acting upwards on the ball. This force is known as the **magnus force** and the effect this force produces is called the **magnus effect**.

Figure 85 represents in simplified form the situation that occurs when a ball is hit with slice or bottom spin. The magnus effect opposes the effect of gravity, so that a ball hit with slice is likely to stay in the air for longer than if it had been hit without spin.

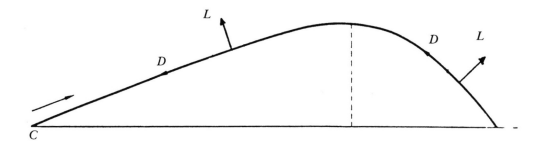

Figure 85: The effect of slice on trajectory of a golf ball

This is a particularly important feature in golf where the ball is hit with an angled blade that gives it slice. The spin keeps the ball in the air for longer than if hit at the same angle without spin. The ball travels further because it is in the air longer. In the early phases of a golf drive, the magnus force created by the spin is just enough to balance the downward force of gravity. Instead of following a curved parabolic pathway, the golf ball travels in a straight line for some time after it has been hit. As air resistance slows the ball down, so the magnus force is reduced and the golf ball falls steeply to the ground towards the end of its flight path (Figure 85).

Top Spin

Top spin is produced by hitting the ball forwards while the racket or bat is being moved upwards. The spin produces a magnus force that acts downwards, making the ball dip in flight (see Figure 86). In tennis, a ball hit with top spin also tends to bounce higher than normally expected. As well as falling to the ground more steeply, the ball hit with top spin is travelling faster when it hits the ground. These two factors combine to give the ball its characteristic high bounce.

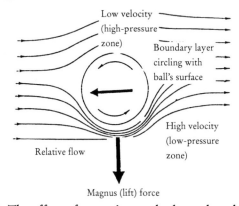

Figure 86: The effect of top spin on the boundary layer (side view)

Side Spin

This is most often seen in football (eg in swerving free kicks) and in golf (eg when the ball is hooked or sliced). Look again at Figures 84 and 86, this time imagining them to be a top view of a ball that has been hit with side spin.

Whether the ball is given top, bottom or side spin, the magnus effect will be greater when the ball spins about an axis that is perpendicular to the direction in which the ball is travelling. No magnus effect will result when the ball spins about an axis that is parallel with the direction in which the ball is travelling.

6.6 Recap and Key Points

In this chapter you have seen how the tangent release principle can help you to predict or correct the flight path of an object. You have also considered the forces of drag and lift and the factors that affect how much drag or lift a body experiences. You have examined how these forces affect the flight path of an object. You have also considered the special case of the spinning ball and the magnus force it creates. This information can be used to produce a simple analysis framework for sporting situations where objects are in flight. This framework is presented in the following section.

What are you trying to do?

If objects or performers are projected into the air, think about the tangent release principle. To identify the object's initial direction:

- draw the arc along which it travelled prior to release
- identify the centre of the circle and the point of release
- draw a line from the centre of the circle to the release point
- remember that the tangent at release is perpendicular to this radial line.

If it involves **objects in flight** and you wish to **change the amount of drag force**, think about the:

- velocity
- shape of the moving object (streamlining)
- cross-surface area
- mass.

Factors	To Increase Drag	To Decrease Drag
Velocity	Increase velocity	Reduce velocity
Shape of object	Less streamlined	More streamlined
Cross-surface area	Increase the area	Decrease the area

The effect of a drag force is greater on a small mass and less on a large mass.

If it involves **objects in flight** and you wish to **change the amount of lift force**, think about the:

- velocity
- area inclined to air flow
- coefficient of lift (shape and angle of attack).

Factors	To Increase Drag	To Decrease Drag
Velocity	Increase velocity	Reduce velocity
Area inclined to air flow	Keep large	Keep small
Coefficient of lift	Optimise ratio between drag and lift	Increase drag whilst reducing lift

If it involves **objects in flight** and you wish to identify the **type of spin** (or predict the effect), think about:

- the direction in which the force acts.

Type of Spin	Direction in Which Force Acts	Effect of Spin
Top spin	Downward force	Dipping, flat trajectory
Back spin/slice	Upward force	Lift, looping trajectory
Side spin	Sideways force	Sideways swerve

To check your understanding of the concepts described in this chapter, try the following self tester.

SELF TESTER FOR CHAPTER SIX

1   Compare the two release points shown below and draw in the probable flight paths of the ball in each case:

 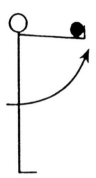

Figure 87: Predicting flight paths

2   Expert downhill skiers crouch as they ski down the mountain. Name the two factors which reduce the drag force acting on them:

   •

   •

3   Cyclists experience drag force as they pedal along. Explain whether a cyclist is likely to experience more or less drag force as the speed increases:

Continued...

4 List the factors that affect profile drag force:

-

-

-

-

5 Identify a situation where a performer needs to reduce profile drag force (use your sport if possible). Where appropriate describe how the performer could improve and reduce profile drag force:

6 Complete the following paragraph:

The _____ of lift is a number expressing how well an object can create lift force in an air flow. The _____ of lift is affected by the _____ of the object relative to the air flow. The _____ of the object also affects the _____ of lift. In many events such as discus, the performer must optimise the ratio between the amount of _____ force generated and the _____ force created.

7 Explain the effect that increased velocity has on the lift force on an object:

8 List the factors that affect lift force:

-

-

-

-

9 Identify a situation where a performer needs to increase lift force (use your sport if possible). Describe how the performer could improve technique and reduce drag force:

10 Describe the sort of spin imparted to the ball to produce the effects described below:

- A free kick in soccer, where the ball swerves sideways around the wall and into the net:

- A low, flat return played in tennis:

What sort of spin has not been described?

What effect is produced by giving the ball this sort of spin?

Now turn over.

1   *Compare the two release points shown below and draw in the probable flight paths of the ball in each case:*

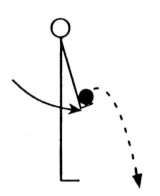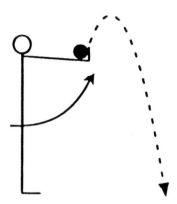

2   *Expert downhill skiers crouch as they ski down the mountain. Name the two factors which reduce the drag force acting on them:*

   • *The cross-sectional area facing the air flow is reduced.*

   • *It creates a streamlined shape.*

3   *Cyclists experience drag force as they pedal along. Explain whether a cyclist is likely to experience more or less drag force as the speed increases:*

   Up to a certain critical value, drag force increases as velocity increases, so the cyclist could expect to experience a greater drag force. Remember that drag force is proportional to the square of the velocity with which the fluid passes the object. If the cyclist's velocity doubled, the drag force would quadruple.

4   *List the factors that affect profile drag force:*

   • *Velocity.*

   • *Cross-sectional area.*

   • *Streamlining.*

   • *Fluid density.*

5   *Identify a situation where a performer needs to reduce profile drag force (use your sport if possible). Where appropriate describe how the performer could improve and reduce profile drag force:*

   Remember that drag will be reduced when:

   • *velocity decreases (or when velocity exceeds the critical value)*

   • *cross-sectional area decreases*

   • *the performer is streamlined*

   • *the fluid density reduces (not usually within the performer's control).*

   Your modifications should be based on these principles, but you will probably need to check the details with an experienced coach in your sport.

6 *Complete the following paragraph:*

*The **coefficient** of lift is a number expressing how well an object can create lift force in an air flow. The **coefficient** of lift is affected by the **angle** of the object relative to the air flow. The **shape** of the object also affects the **coefficient** of lift. In many events such as discus, the performer must optimise the ratio between the amount of **drag** force generated and the **lift** force created.*

7 *Explain the effect that increased velocity has on the lift force on an object:*

Increasing the velocity within which an object moves through a fluid would increase the amount of lift force that object generated.

8 *List the factors that affect lift force:*

*   *The coefficient of lift (shape and angle of attack).*
*   *Velocity.*
*   *Surface area.*
*   *Air density.*

9 *Identify a situation where a performer needs to increase lift force (use your sport if possible). Describe how the performer could improve technique and reduce drag force:*

Your modifications should be based on the above principles but you will need to check them with a senior coach in your sport.

10 *Describe the sort of spin imparted to the ball to produce the effects described below:*

*   *A free kick in soccer, where the ball swerves sideways around the wall and into the net:*

    The player makes the ball swerve by putting side spin on it.
*   *A low, flat return played in tennis:*

    A low trajectory is characteristic of a topspin shot.

What sort of spin has not been described?

The spin that has not been mentioned is bottom spin.

What effect is produced by giving the ball this sort of spin?

The effect of bottom spin is best seen in a golf drive.

If you had any difficulty with this self tester, go back and reread the relevant parts before moving on to the next chapter.

6.7 Further Help

Bartlett, RM (1997) **Introduction to sports biomechanics.**
London, E & FN Spon. ISBN 0-4192-08402.
Chapter 2: Movement (kinematic) Considerations (pp69–73)
and Chapter 4: Fluid Mechanics and Energetics (pp124–142).

Daish, CB (1972) **The physics of ball games.**
London, English Universities Press. ISBN 0-340-053992.

Dyson, GHG (1986) **Dyson's mechanics of athletics.**
8th edition. London, Hodder and Stoughton Educational. ISBN 0-340-39172-3.
Chapter 2: Motion (pp4–13) and Chapter 5: Angular Motion (pp65–122).

Hall, S (1991) **Basic biomechanics.** St Louis MS, Mosby. ISBN 0-8016-2087-2.
Chapter 14: The importance of fluids (pp416–447).

Hay, JG (1993) **The biomechanics of sports techniques.**
4th edition. London, Prentice Hall. ISBN 0-13-084534-5.
Chapter 3: Linear Kinematics (pp31–46) and Chapter 7: Fluid Mechanics (pp178–197).

The Complete Jigsaw

7.0 Introduction

Each chapter in this pack has dealt with a different topic and has presented various pieces of the sports mechanics jigsaw. At the end of each chapter, these jigsaw pieces have been fitted together to form part of a framework. These frameworks are intended to help you look more carefully at your sport and use your biomechanical knowledge to analyse and improve performance.

In this chapter, all the analysis frameworks are presented again for easy reference and to help you complete the mechanics jigsaw. Before you use the completed framework for any sort of analysis, it is important to spend time on a first and vital step – specifying exactly what it is you are trying to do. Select a specific aspect of performance and explain your aim in mechanical terms. This will help you identify which parts of the framework you need to use.

Then work through the framework until you find the section that answers your question.

7.1 Process of Analysis

1   If it involves **analysing linear motion,** think about:

- **what** forces are involved

- **where** the point of application of the force is

- **in what direction** the force acts (force must be applied through the object's centre of gravity to produce linear motion)

- **how much** force is being applied.

2   If it involves **analysing stability,** think about the:

- size of the base
- height of the centre of gravity
- position of the line of gravity
- mass.

Factors	To be Unstable	To be Stable
Size of base	As small as possible	As large as possible
Height of centre of gravity	As high as possible	As low as possible
Position of line of gravity	Near edge of base	Far from edge of base
Mass	As little as possible	As big as possible

3   If it involves **starting things moving,** think about:

- the size of the object to be moved
- the number of joints used
- when the joints are used
- how the joints are used.

Factors	To Start Large Objects Moving Slowly	To Start Small Objects Moving Quickly
Number of joints used	All joints	All joints
When the joints are used	All joints at once	In sequence (large to small)
How the joints are used	Use maximum range	Use maximum range

4 If it involves **stopping things moving**, think about:

- the size (and velocity) of the object to be stopped
- how the joints are used
- the stopping time
- other apparatus that increases stopping time.

Factors	To Slow Fast-moving Small Objects	To Slow Fast-moving Large Objects
Stopping time	Use in sequence (small to large)	Use in sequence (small to large)
How joints are used	Maximise to increase safety	Maximise to increase safety
Other apparatus	Padded gloves, net	Large spaces, brakes, crash mats

5 If it involves rotation, identify the:

- axis of rotation
- point of application of force
- direction in which the force acts.

Think about the:

- amount of force required
- perpendicular distance from line of action of the force to axis of rotation
- moment of inertia of the rotating object.

Factors	To Decrease Rotation	To Increase Rotation
Amount of force	Reduce the force acting in same direction as rotation	Increase the force acting in same direction as rotation
Perpendicular distance from line of action of that force to axis of rotation	Reduce the distance	Increase the distance
Moment of inertia	Increase	Decrease

6   If objects of performers are projected into the air, think about the tangent release principle. To identify the object's initial direction:

- draw the arc along which it travelled prior to release

- identify the centre of the circle and the point of release

- draw a line from the centre of the circle to the release point

- remember that the tangent at release is perpendicular to this radial line.

If it involves objects in flight and you wish to change the amount of drag force, think about the:

- velocity

- shape of the moving object (streamlining)

- cross-surface area

- mass.

Factors	To Increase Drag	To Decrease Drag
Velocity	Increase velocity	Reduce velocity
Shape of object	Less streamlined	More streamlined
Cross-surface area	Increase the area	Decrease the area
Mass	Small mass	Large mass

7   If it involves **objects in flight** and you wish to **change the amount of lift force**, think about the:

- velocity

- area inclined to air flow

- coefficient of lift (shape and angle of attack)

Factors	To Increase Lift	To Decrease Lift
Velocity	Increase velocity	Decrease velocity
Area inclined to air flow	Keep large	Keep small
Coefficient of lift	Optimise ratio between drag and lift	Increase drag while reducing lift

8   If it involves objects in flight and you wish to identify the **type of spin** (or predict the effect), think about:

  • the direction in which the force acts.

Type of Spin	Direction in which Force Acts	Effect of Spin
Top spin	Downward force	Dipping, flat trajectory
Back spin/slice	Upward force	Lift, looping trajectory
Side spin	Sideways force	Sideways swerve

7.2 What Next?

You should now have grasped a number of basic mechanical principles and acquired some guidelines to help you analyse movements in your sport more objectively. This should enable you to be more confident in deciding whether any changes should be made to a particular technique to make it more effective. You may now wish to try the multiple choice questions and the case study provided in Appendix C. These may help you to provide some evidence for assessment.

This is the beginning of the road to helping you to develop your analytic skills and so become a more effective coach. You now need to try to apply the skills to your own sport situation. The NCF Coach Workshop *Observation, Analysis and Video* will add to your knowledge and identify additional ways of analysing performance.

An understanding of sports mechanics and analysis is just one part of the armoury in helping you to understand sports and sports performance.

Recommended NCF Coach Workshops and resources (complimentary with the corresponding workshop) covering all aspects of coaching include:

NCF Coach Workshop	Resource
Analysing your Coaching	Analysing your Coaching (home study)
Coaching Children and Young People	Coaching Young Performers
Coaching Disabled Performers	Coaching Disabled Performers (home study)
Coaching Methods and Communication	Successful Coach
Fitness and Training	Physiology and Performance
Fuelling Performers	Fuelling Performers
Goal-setting and Planning	Planning Coaching Programmes (home study)
Good Practice and Child Protection	Protecting Children (home study)
Improving Practices and Skill	Improving Practices and Skill
Injury Prevention and Management	Sports Injury
Motivation and Mental Toughness	Psychology and Performance
Observation, Analysis and Video	Observation, Analysis and Video

Other recommended NCF texts – *An Introduction to the Structure of the Body* and *An Introduction to Sports Physiology*.

Details of all NCF resources are available from:

Coachwise Ltd
Units 2/3, Chelsea Close
Off Amberley Road
Armley
Leeds
LS12 4HW
Tel: 0113 231 1310
Fax: 0113 231 9606

E-mail: enquiries@coachwise.ltd.uk
Internet: www.1st4sport.com

The NCF also produces a technical journal – *Faster, Higher, Stronger (FHS)* and an information update service for coaches (*in*FORM). Details of these services are available from:

The National Coaching Foundation
114 Cardigan Road
Headingley
Leeds
LS6 3BJ
Tel: 0113 274 4802
Fax: 0113 275 5019
E-mail: coaching@ncf.org.uk
Internet: www.ncf.org.uk

For direct bookings on NCF workshops at Premier Coaching Centres, please contact:

Workshop Booking Centre
Units 2/3, Chelsea Close
Off Amberley Road
Armley
Leeds
LS12 4HW
Tel: 0845 601 3054
Fax: 0113 231 9606

7.3 Further Help

Bartlett, RM (1997) **Introduction to sports biomechanics.**
London, E & FN Spon. ISBN 0-4192-08402.

Hall, S (1991) **Basic biomechanics.** St Louis MS, Mosby. ISBN 0-8016-2087-2.

Hay, JG (1993) **The biomechanics of sports techniques.**
4th edition. London, Prentice Hall. ISBN 0-13-084534-5.

For details of all NCF workshops, contact your nearest Regional Training Unit or home countries office:

East	Tel: 01234 262063/261547 Fax 01234 214457	**East Mids**	Tel: 01509 223493 Fax: 01509 223950
West Mids	Tel: 0121 414 3379/414 3890 Fax 0121 414 7645	**South East**	Tel: 01323 411186 Fax: 01323 644653
London	Tel: 020 7594 9069 Fax: 020 7594 9070	**South West**	Tel: 01225 444823 Fax: 01225 461547
North	Tel: 0191 374 7820 Fax: 0191 374 7434	**Wales**	Tel: 029 20300500/300572 Fax: 029 20300600
North West	Tel: 01695 584657 Fax: 01695 584710	**Northern Ireland**	Tel: 028 9038 1222 Fax: 028 9068 2757
South	Tel: 01628 475510/488609 Fax: 01628 475512	**Scotland**	Tel: 0131 317 1091/317 7200 Fax: 0131 317 7202
Yorkshire	Tel: 0113 283 7579/283 1763 Fax: 0113 283 3170		

Glossary of Terms

Acceleration	Speeding up or slowing down. Rate of change of velocity per unit of time. Measured in metres per second squared.
Angular momentum	Amount of angular motion of a body, limb, object. Product of moment of inertia and angular velocity.
Angular motion	Circular movement. Movement of a body, limb, object in an arc around an axis.
Angular velocity	Speed of rotation. Rate of change of angular displacement. Usually measured in degrees per second or revolutions per second.
Anterior-posterior axis	An axis of rotation passing from the front to the back of the body.
Axis of rotation	Imaginary line around which rotation of a body, limb, object occurs.
Base of support	Part or parts of the body which support it, plus the area between those parts.
Biomechanics	Scientific study of human motion based on mechanics, physics, mathematics, anatomy.
Centre of gravity	Imaginary point around which the mass of a body, limb, object is balanced. The point at which the body's weight can be considered to act.
Dynamic equilibrium	Used to describe an object or person travelling with constant velocity.
Equilibrium	Objects or people are in a state of equilibrium when their motion is not changing.
Force	Push or pull which causes or tends to cause motion. Measured in newtons.
Friction	A force which opposes the relative motion of two bodies in contact.

Gravity	The attractive force exerted by the earth on all objects surrounding it.
Impulse	Application of force over a period of time which changes the velocity of a body or object.
Inertia	Measure of resistance to change, the state of motion.
Instability	Lack of balance, steadiness.
Joint	Place where two bones come together.
Joint range of motion	Amount of possible movement of a body segment about a joint. Measured in degrees.
Linear momentum	Amount of motion in a straight line. Product of mass and velocity.
Linear motion	Movement in a straight line. Produced when forces act through centre of gravity.
Line of gravity	Imaginary line from the centre of gravity straight down to the ground.
Mass	Quantity of matter in a body or object. Measure of resistance to linear motion measured in kilograms.
Moment	See Torque.
Moment of inertia	How hard it is to make a body, limb, object start to rotate, change speed of rotation, or stop rotating. Measure of resistance to change in angular motion. Product of mass and the square of the distance from the centre of gravity of the body part to the axis of rotation.
Momentum	Amount of motion. Product of body's mass and velocity.

Newton's First Law of Motion	A body will continue in its state of rest or of uniform motion in a straight line, unless acted upon by some external force.
Newton's Second Law of Motion	The rate of change of momentum of a body is proportional to the force acting upon the body and is in the direction of the applied force.
Newton's Third Law of Motion	For every force acting upon a body there is a concurrent force of the same magnitude exerted by the body in the opposite direction.
Range of motion	See Joint range of motion.
Scalar quantity	A quantity which has size only.
Stability	State of being not easily moved.
Static equilibrium	Used to describe a stationary object or person.
Streamlining	Minimising and smoothing the leading surface area of a body or object so as to lessen resistance to motion.
Torque	Term used for force in angular motion. Force applied away from the axis of rotation which produces angular motion. Product of force and the perpendicular distance from the axis of rotation to the point of application of the force.
Transfer of momentum	Process of redistribution of angular momentum within a body.
Vector quantity	A quantity which has size and direction.
Velocity	Speed in a certain direction. The rate of change of displacement. Measured in metres per second.

Multiple Choice Questions and Case Study

If you wish to check your own understanding and knowledge, complete the following questions. Shade in the box alongside your chosen answer(s). For each statement there may be more than one correct response.

1 What is meant by force?

- ❑ a   It is what gets things moving or stops things moving.
- ❑ b   The speed of movement in sport.
- ❑ c   The pushing or pulling effect that changes an object's state of rest.
- ❑ d   The strength of a performer to overcome obstacles.

2 There are several things to remember about gravity:

- ❑ a   Gravity pushes all objects away from each other.
- ❑ b   The greater your mass, the greater the pulling effect of gravity.
- ❑ c   The effect of gravity becomes greater as you move away from the centre of the earth.
- ❑ d   Gravity exerts a downward pull on every particle of matter in your body.

3 The force that operates when an object is moving is called:

- ❑ a   negative resistance
- ❑ b   static friction
- ❑ c   dynamic friction
- ❑ d   velocity force.

4 Which four major forces are likely to influence any sporting situation?

- ❑ a   Friction, external forces, weight of performer, air resistance.
- ❑ b   Static friction, gravity, internal forces, dynamic friction.
- ❑ c   Normal force, static friction, stability, muscular force.
- ❑ d   Gravity, friction, air resistance, muscular forces.

5 Dynamic equilibrium describes:

- ❑ a   an object or person travelling at a range of speeds in the same direction
- ❑ b   an object or person travelling at the same speed in the same direction
- ❑ c   the speed of an object compared to the speed of a person
- ❑ d   an object or person travelling at the same speed but continually changing direction.

6 Which of the following factors cause instability?

❏ a High centre of gravity.

❏ b Large mass.

❏ c Large size of base.

❏ d Small size of base.

7 What is the product of a force (F) and the length of time over which the force is applied (t)?

❏ a Momentum.

❏ b Duration.

❏ c Speed.

❏ d Impulse.

8 You can increase the time for which force is applied by using:

❏ a all the joints and muscles in sequence – smallest to largest

❏ b all the joints and muscles in sequence – largest to smallest

❏ c a large range of movement in each joint

❏ d one muscle or joint at a time.

9 Which of the following is/are true?

❏ a The longer force is applied, the less the change in momentum.

❏ b The greater the force applied, the greater the change in momentum.

❏ c The shorter the time of force, the less the change in momentum.

❏ d The greater the force applied, the less the change in momentum.

10 Objects can be slowed down safely and effectively by:

❏ a decreasing the time taken to slow the object down

❏ b increasing the time taken to slow the object down

❏ c cushioning the force of the object

❏ d using a hard surface to stop the object.

11 To get small objects moving quickly, use:

❏ a all joints, in sequence large to small, using maximum range

❏ b all joints, at once, using maximum range

❏ c all joints, in sequence small to large, using maximum range

❏ d selected joints, in sequence large to small, using maximum range.

12 Which of the following actions use the stated axes:

❑ a   Football kicking (longitudinal), bending forward to pick up a ball (transverse), stretching to the left (anterior posterior).

❑ b   Football kicking (transverse), bending forward to pick up a ball (transverse), stretching to the right (transverse).

❑ c   Football kicking (longitudinal), bending forward to pick up a ball (anterior posterior), stretching to the right (transverse).

❑ d   Football kicking (transverse), bending forward to pick up a ball (transverse), stretching to the left (anterior posterior).

13 Torque refers to the:

❑ a   turning effect produced by a force acting at some distance from an axis of rotation

❑ b   the maximum force causing a turning effect

❑ c   line of action of the force extending indefinitely in the direction of the force

❑ d   maximum rotation produced by a force.

14 The resistance of an object to start rotating (or change its rate of rotation) about a particular axis is referred to as its:

❑ a   amount of force

❑ b   static force

❑ c   perpendicular distance

❑ d   moment of inertia.

15 Drag force in flight can be decreased by:

❑ a   increasing velocity, more streamlining, increase the area, large mass

❑ b   reducing velocity, less streamlining, decrease area, small mass

❑ c   reducing velocity, more streamlining, decrease area, large mass

❑ d   increasing velocity, less streamlining, constant area, large mass.

16 To increase lift:

❑ a   optimise the ratio between drag and lift

❑ b   decrease velocity

❑ c   increase velocity

❑ d   keep area inclined to the air flow small.

17 The coefficient of lift:

- ❑ a   indicates how quickly a ball rises after being hit
- ❑ b   is the ratio of velocity to height above the ground
- ❑ c   is the ratio of surface area to air density
- ❑ d   indicates how well an object can create lift force in airflow.

18 Which of the following are true?

- ❑ a   A flat, dipping trajectory results from top spin which causes a downward force.
- ❑ b   Sideways swerve results from slice which causes side spin.
- ❑ c   Back spin results in an upward force.
- ❑ d   Spin affects the velocity of the object, not the trajectory.

19 To increase rotation:

- ❑ a   decrease the moment of inertia
- ❑ b   decrease the force acting in the same direction as rotation
- ❑ c   increase the moment of inertia
- ❑ d   increase the force acting in the same direction as rotation.

20 The factors which affect the flight of an object include:

- ❑ a   its height above the ground
- ❑ b   the direction in which a force is applied
- ❑ c   the amount of force applied
- ❑ d   the point of application of the force.

Answers can be found on Page 206.

Case Study

Select a technique (or number of techniques) on which you are currently working with your performers. Identify the forces that are operating and illustrate these using appropriate diagrams. For one of your performers, use these diagrams to show how performance could be improved. Explain the action which needs to be taken to make these improvements. Following a training programme to improve these aspects, comment on its effectiveness.

Answers to multiple choice questions:

1: a & c	5: b	9: b & c	13: a	17: d
2: b & d	6: a & d	10: b & c	14: d	18: a & c
3: c	7: d	11: a	15: c	19: a & d
4: d	8: b	12: d	16: a & c	20: b, c & d

Appendix C

National Occupational Standards for Coaching, Teaching and Instructing

The National Occupational Standards for Coaching, Teaching and Instructing (NOS) are based around a number of competencies associated with planning, delivering and evaluating coaching sessions and programmes. The standards are used as part of national govening bodiesí coach education awards and as the definition of competence for Scottish/National Vocational Qualifications (S/NVQs) in coaching, teaching and instructing. S/NVQs at Levels 2 and 3 are available in a number of sports. The NCF has developed its Coach Development Programme around these standards. NCF workshops and resources aim to provide the underpinning knowledge for coaches who wish to meet the competencies of the standards. They also give coaches guidelines on how to apply this knowledge to their coaching practice.

This resource *An Introduction to Sports Mechanics* has been designed to support the following unit of the Level 3 NOS:

Unit D48 Apply biomechanical principles to performance
D48.1 Analyse the biomechnanical aspects of the participantís performance
D48.2 Identify and propose methods of improving biomechanical performance
D48.3 Implement and evaluate methods of improving biomechanical performance

For further information on the National Occupational Standards for Coaching, Teaching and Instructing at Level 3, contact the National Coaching Foundation or SPRITO at the following addresses:

The National Coaching Foundation
114 Cardigan Road
Headingley
Leeds
LS6 3BJ

Tel: 0113 274 4802
Fax: 0113 275 5019
E-mail: coaching@ncf.org.uk

The National Training Organisation for
Sport, Recreation and Allied
Occupations
24 Stephenson Way
London
NW1 2HD

Tel: 020 7388 7755
Fax: 020 7388 9733
E-mail: the.nto@sprito.org.uk